OVER THE
FOOTLIGHTS

OVER THE FOOTLIGHTS
AND OTHER FANCIES
BY STEPHEN LEACOCK

LONDON: JOHN LANE THE BODLEY HEAD LTD
MCMXXIII

First Published in 1923

MADE AND PRINTED IN GREAT BRITAIN BY MORRISON AND GIBB LTD., EDINBURGH

CONTENTS

OVER THE FOOTLIGHTS

OTHER FANCIES

OVER THE FOOTLIGHTS

I—"Cast up by the Sea," a Seacoast Melodrama

(As Thrown up for Thirty Cents. Period, 1880)

EVERYBODY who has reached or passed middle age looks back with affection to that splendid old melodrama, *Cast up by the Sea*. Perhaps it wasn't called exactly that. It may have been named *Called back from the Dead*, or *Broken up by the Wind*, or *Buried Alive in the Snow*, or anything of the sort. In fact, I believe it was played under about forty different names in fifty different forms. But it was always the same good old melodrama of the New England coast, with the farmhouse and the yellow fields running down to the sea, and the lighthouse right at the end of the farm, with the rocks and the sea beyond, looking for trouble.

Before the cinematograph had addled the human brain and the radio broadcast had disintegrated the human mind, you could go and see *Cast up by the Sea* any Saturday afternoon in any great American city for thirty cents ; you got a thrill from it that lasted twenty years. For thirty cents you had an orchestra chair on the ground floor, where you could sit and eat pea-nuts and study the programme till the play began. After it had begun you couldn't eat any more ; you were too excited.

The first thing everybody used to do in studying the programme was to see how many years elapsed between the acts ; because in those days everybody used to find it wiser to go out between the acts— for air. And the more years that elapsed and the more acts there were, the more air they could get. Some of the plays used to have ten acts, and the people got out nine times. Nowadays this is all changed. People talk now of the unity of the drama, and in some of the plays to-day there is a deliberate announcement on the programme that reads, " Between Acts II and III the curtain will be merely lowered and raised again." We wouldn't have stood for that in 1880. We needed our two years between the acts. We had a use for it.

As I say, it was necessary to study the programme. Nobody had yet invented that system of marking the characters " in the order of their appearance." You had to try and learn up the whole lot before the play began. You couldn't really. But you began conscientiously enough. Hiram Haycroft, a farmer ; Martha, his wife ; Hope, their daughter ; Phœbe, a girl help ; Zeke, a hired man ; Rube, also

4

a hired man—and by that time you had just forgotten the farmer's own name, and looked back for it when just then——

Up went the curtain with a long stately roll, two men at the side hoisting it, and there you were, looking at the farmstead by the sea.

Notice how quick and easy and attractive that old-fashioned beginning was. One minute you were eating pea-nuts and studying the programme, and the next minute the play had begun. There was none of that agonizing stuff that precedes the moving pictures of to-day; no "Authorized by the Board of Censors of the State of New York." The world and New York State were so good in 1880 that they had never heard of a censor. Nor was there any announcement of something else altogether, heralded as "A great big compelling Life Drama—next week."

If the moving-picture people could have been in control (forty years before their time) they would have announced the farm and lighthouse play with a written panegyric on what they were going to show: "A gripping Heart Drama, in which the foam of the sea and the eerie of the spindrift carry to the heart a tale of true love battled by the wind—next Thursday."

But if they had worked that stuff on an audience of 1880 it would have gone out and taken another drink, and never came back until next Thursday.

So the play began at once. There was the farmhouse, or at least the porch and door, at the right-hand side of the stage, all bathed in sunlight (yellow gas), and the grass plot and the road in the centre, and the yellow wheat (quite a little bunch of it) at the left, and the fields reaching back till they hit the painted curtain with the lighthouse and the rocks and the sea.

Everybody who looked at that painted curtain and saw that lighthouse knew that it wasn't there for nothing. There'd be something doing from that all right, and when they looked back at the programme and saw that Act IV was marked, " In the Lighthouse Tower—Midnight," they got the kind of thrill that you can never get by a mere announcement that there is going to be a " gripping Heart Drama next Tues., Thurs. and Sat."

Surely enough there would be something doing with that lighthouse. Either the heroine thrown off it or the hero thrown over it—anyway, something good.

But for the moment all is peace and sunlight on the seashore farm. There is no one on the stage but two men on the left, evidently Zeke and Rube, the hired men. They've got scythes and they are cutting the little patch of wheat over at the edge

6

of the stage. Just imagine it. *Real* wheat ; they're
actually cutting it ! Upon my word, those stage
effects of 1880 were simply wonderful! I do wish
that "Doug" Fairbanks and those fellows who
work so hard to give us thrills could realize what
we used to get in 1880 by seeing Zeke and Rube
cutting real wheat on the left-hand side of the
stage.

Then they speak. You can't really hear what
they say—but it sounds like this :

Zeke says, "I swam b'gosh heck b'gosh gum, yak!
yak ! "

And Rube answers, " Heck gosh b'gum, yes, yak !
yak ! "

And they both laugh.

These words probably have a meaning, but you
don't need it. The people are still moving into
their seats, and this is just the opening of the play.
It's a mere symbol. It stands for New England
dialect, farm life, and honesty of character.

Presently Rube gets articulate. He quits reaping,
and he says :

" So Miss Hope'll be coming back this morning."

" Yes, sir, that she will. A whole year now it'll
be that she's been to boarding-school."

And Rube says :

" Yep, a whole year come Gurdlemas."

Rube and Zeke have a calendar all their own.

7

" She'll be a growd-up lady now all right."

" Yes, sir, and as purty as a pitcher, I'll be bound, by heck! "

They whet their scythes with a clang, and out comes Martha, the farmer's wife, and Phœbe, the help, from the porch on the right. With them comes a freckled boy, evidently the younger son of the farm family. This freckled boy is in all the melodramas. It is his business to get his ears boxed, mislay the will, lose the mortgage, forget to post the letters, and otherwise mix up the plot.

" Do you see the buggy yet, Rube ? Can you see them coming yet, Zeke ? "

Zeke and Rube hop about making gestures of looking down the road, their hands up over their eyes.

" Not yet, Missus, but they'll be along right soon now."

" There they are! " calls Phœbe, " coming along down in the hollow."

There is great excitement at once. Martha cries, " Land's sake, if it ain't Hope all right! " and boxes the freckled boy's ears. The others run to and fro saying, " Here they come ! " so as to get the audience worked up with excitement, at the height of which there comes the actual clatter of the horse's hoofs, and the next moment a horse

8

and buggy, a real horse and buggy, drives on to the stage. That clattering horse coming on to the stage was always one of the great effects in 1880— a real horse with real harness, and with added anxiety for fear that the horse would misbehave himself when he came on.

The buggy stops with a lot of shouting of " Whoa there ! "—intended to keep the horse lively. If they didn't shout at it this stage horse was apt to subside into a passive melancholy not suited for the drama.

So here is the farmer sitting in the buggy in a suit of store clothes and a black slouch hat, and beside him is Hope, his daughter, just home from boarding-school. How sweet and fresh she looks in her New England sun hat with the flowers on it ! I don't know what they did to the girls in the boarding-schools of 1880—some line of algebra, perhaps— to make them look so fresh. There are none like them now.

Hope leaps out in one spring and kisses her mother in one bound, and she cries, " Well, mother ! Well, Phœbe ! Why, Zeke ! Why, Rube ! " They all circulate and hop and dance about, saying, " Well, Miss Hope ! well, I never ! " And all the while there's the sunshine in the yellow fields and the red hollyhocks beside the porch, and light and happiness everywhere.

9

You'd think, would you not, that that old home-stead represented the high-water mark of happiness ? And so it does. But wait a bit. Before long they'll start trouble enough. All the audience know in advance that that farm will be mortgaged and the farmer ruined, and Hope driven from home—oh, there's lots of trouble coming. Trouble was the proper business of the melodrama. So presently they all get through their congratulations and Hope has embraced everybody, and the farmer's wife has got off two jokes about the size of Boston, and then the freckled boy wants to take Hope away to see the brindle cow, and they all fade away off the stage except the farmer and his wife.

And right away the whole tone of the play changes, just like that.

The farmer stands alone with his wife.

And Martha comes over to him and puts her hand timidly on his shoulder. The joy has gone out of her face.

" Hiram," she says, " Lawyer Ellwood's agent was here this morning."

The farmer fairly humps into his shoulders with anger.

" Ay," he snarls.

" And, Hiram, Lawyer Ellwood wants his money."

" Ay ! he wants his money, does he ? Curse him ! "

The farmer's fist is clenched and there's a scowl on his face.

"He says, Hiram, that it's got to be paid to-morrow. Oh, Hiram, we can't never pay it."

Martha puts her apron up to her face and sobs.

The farmer turns and shakes his clenched fist at the scenery away off to the left.

"Curse him!" he rages. "Ay, curse him! This three years he has thrown a blight across our life."

"You was friends oncet, Hiram," sobs Martha again, "years ago, before he went to the city, you was friends."

"Friends!" raves the farmer, "a fine friend, drawing me on with his schemes of money and profit. 'To make my fortune,' he said. A fine fortune—ruin, ruin, it meant—till I had signed this and signed that, till it was all mortgaged away, and till he held me, as he thought, in the hollow of his hand. Martha, if that man stood before me now, by the God that lives, I could choke him with these hands!"

Hiram makes a gesture so terrible and yet so passionate that the one hope of the audience in the top gallery is that Lawyer Ellwood will happen along right now and get choked.

Martha tries to dry her eyes.

"Nay, Hiram, you mustn't talk like that. Those

are evil thoughts. It is God's will, Hiram, and it must be right. But we can't never pay."

"Not pay!" shouts Hiram, "who says I can't pay? I *can* pay, and when that man comes to-morrow I *can* throw the money in his face. Look, Martha, there it is!"

Hiram Haycroft draws a great wallet from his pocket and slaps it down on the palm of his hand.

"Two thousand dollars, every cent of his accursed debt. Martha, it will mean poverty and hard times for us where all was plenty, but, thank God! it can be paid."

"Why, Hiram!"

"I've raised it, Martha. I've sold the stock. I've parted with this and I've pledged that—everything but the roof above our heads is sold or pledged. But this accursed mortgage can be paid."

"Oh, Hiram!"

"It will mean hard times again, hard and bitter times——"

"I don't mind that, Hiram"—and Martha puts her hands up to her husband's neck—"we've borne it together before, and we can bear it together again; but oh, Hiram, if only our boy Jack had been spared to us, I could have borne it so easily then."

Martha begins to cry.

"There, there, Martha," says the farmer, "you

mustn't lay it so to heart. The sea has taken him, mother, as it has taken many a brave lad before him——"

"The sea, the sea!" groans Martha; "I see it there so bright and calm in the sunlight. But will it give me back my boy? Three years this day, Hiram, since he left us. I can feel his good-bye kiss still on my cheek. And since then no word, never a word."

Hiram draws his wife to him to comfort her.

"Come, mother, come into the house; we mustn't show sad faces for Hope's home-coming—come——"

They go in through the wooden porch under the flowers on the right, leaving the audience sad and disturbed. That infernal lawyer! But they were all alike in 1880. Show them a sunlit farm and a happy family and they clap a mortgage on it at sight. And to think that Farmer Haycroft and his wife had lost their only son at sea—that calm, blue sea in the back curtain with the sunlight on it.

In fact the play is getting too sad, so it has to be relieved, and Rube and Phœbe are brought on to the stage again and go through one of those rural love scenes that were used to ease the strain of the melodrama. Rube shambles over to her in a sheepish way, evidently proposing to kiss her, and says :

"Ain't you got nothing for me this morning, Phœb?"

And Phœbe says:

"Go along, you big thing, I've got *that* for you," and swats him over the face with a thistle.

The audience roar with laughter, the strain is removed, and they're ready to get on with the play when Phœbe disappears, with Rube in pursuit.

"Why, mother,"—it is Hope calling,—"where are you, mother?"

"I'm here, daughter," says Martha, reappearing out of the porch.

"I was looking for you all over, mother," says Hope, coming over to her coyly. "I have been wanting so much to talk to you all by ourselves."

"Ah! And I think I can guess something of what that's about." Martha has taken Hope's hand in hers and is patting it, and Hope is looking at the ground and swinging herself about on one heel in a way that in a New England play always symbolized the approach of love.

"And now, Hope, tell me all about it," says the farmer's wife.

"You remember, mother, that I wrote and told you that I had a secret——"

"Yes, dearie, a *great* secret, you said——"

"A secret that I didn't want to put on paper

14

and didn't want to tell to anybody till I could tell it to you first, mother dear."

Hope has snuggled up close to her mother, who is patting her on the shoulder and repeating, " Ay, lass, a great secret, and I'll be bound I can guess a little of what it is. I suppose it means that there is some one—that my little girl——"

She whispers into Hope's ear.

" Oh, mother," Hope goes on, " it's even greater than that. Look, mother, see what's on my hand."

Hope holds out her hand, her face downcast, and not only her mother but even the girls in the gallery can see the plain gold ring that's on her finger. The men in the audience don't get it, but the girls and women explain to them what it is.

" Why, Hope, darling," says Martha, all in a tremble, " what does it mean ? "

" Why, mother, it means—it means "—Hope takes a flying leap into her mother's arms—" it means, mother, that I'm married."

" Married ! "

" Yes, married, mother—last Saturday in Boston, at eleven o'clock in the morning."

" Married ! My little girl married ! "

Martha has to be terribly astonished so as to keep the audience in the same frame of mind. Not at Hope being married the very day she left her finishing school; that was nothing—that was a

15

favourite way of getting married in 1880—but at
the fact that she hadn't told her mother about it.
So Martha keeps repeating:

"Married! My little girl married!"

"It was all in such a hurry, mother—I couldn't
tell you. It all came so sudden——"

Hope is half crying, half smiling.

"But I shouldn't cry, mother, because really
I'm so happy——"

"That's right, darling, and now tell me all about
it."

"We were married in Boston last Saturday,
mother. And, oh, I did so want you to be there,
only it couldn't be. It was all in such a hurry—
because Ned was offered a new ship—just think,
mother, captain of a ship at twenty-one."

"Not a sailor, dearie," says Martha Haycroft in
evident agitation, "don't tell me that your man is
a sailor."

"Why, yes, mother. Ned's been at sea ever since
he was fifteen."

"The sea, the sea!" groans the farmer's wife.
"I see it lying there in the sunlight. I hear it
roaring in the winter wind. When will it give me
back my boy?"

"Mother, you mustn't cry. It was years ago,
and it was God's will; and mother, Ned will only
be at sea a little while longer now—just this one

voyage in his new ship; and listen, mother, Ned's new ship (it's a schooner, mother, and it's Ned's father who owns it, and it's called the *Good Hope*, after me) will be off the coast here this evening, and if Ned can manage it he'll come ashore and see us all; and his father—though I've never seen *him*—will be with Ned. And Ned is to settle down and be a farmer, mother, on a farm beside the sea. His father is a rich lawyer in Boston, mother, and Ned says that his father has a mortgage on a farm right on the seashore just like this, and after this one voyage——"

" A lawyer, a rich lawyer ! "

" Yes, mother, a rich lawyer in Boston; but he once lived in the country, near here, I think, years ago."

" His name ? What name ? "

" Ellwood, mother ; Lawyer Ephraim Ellwood."
Martha breaks from her daughter in alarm.

" No, no, not that; don't say it's that name—Hope, it couldn't be, it can't be ! "

And at that moment the farmer, Hiram Haycroft, steps on to the stage.

" Why, mother ! Why, Hope ! What's—what's all this ? "

Hope (tearfully): " I don't know, father ; I only began to tell Mother a secret——"

" Yes, daughter ! "

" That I—that we—that I am married, father."

" Married, my little girl married ! That don't seem possible. But what's all this ado about, mother, and who's the lucky man that's gone and taken my little girl ? "

Hiram comes over affectionately and takes Hope's two hands.

" Only yesterday, it seems," he says, " that I held you on my knees, little gal, and now to be married."

All the audience waits in a luxury of expectation. They know that the farmer is going to get an awful jolt.

Then he gets it.

" He is the son of a rich Boston lawyer, father, who—has a mortgage on a farm——"

The farmer has dropped Hope's hands, his face is darkening.

" And Ned is to have the farm—Ned Ellwood is his name, father ; see it here."

Hope timidly takes out a paper from her dress.

" Here on my marriage certificate."

But the farmer doesn't hear her. He stands a moment, his fists clenched, then bursts into wild rage.

" Ellwood, Lawyer Ellwood. My daughter marry a son of that man ! By the living God, Hope, sooner than see you married to a son of his, I'd see you lying fathoms deep under the sea beside my son. God hears me say it, and may God so order it ! "

And as Hiram Haycroft stands, with this fateful invocation on his lips, the freckled boy runs on the stage and says :

" Say, Hope, ain't you never coming to see that brindle cow ? "

And with that the curtain slowly falls, and Act I is over.

No wonder that as the curtain falls there's a terrible feeling of sadness and apprehension all over the audience. No wonder that even before the curtain has reached the floor a great many of the men in that 1880 audience have risen and are walking up the aisles to get out of the theatre. They can't stand the strain of it—the thought of the beautiful old New England homestead all brought to sorrow and tragedy like this. It's too much for them. They must have air. They've gone to look for it outside the theatre. Even though the play-bill says that only six hours elapse between Acts I and II (pretty rapid work for 1880), they're taking a chance on it.

So the able-bodied men in the audience go out, leaving behind only the young, the infirm, and the women (women never took anything to drink, anyway, before Prohibition). There is a great sadness over the audience now, because they know by experience that once the old homestead starts going to pieces like this things will go from bad to worse. Even the fact that the orchestra is now playing, " In the Gloaming, oh my Darling," doesn't help things much.

So presently the men come back, and the orchestra is stopped and the gas cut down, and the curtain is hauled away up to the roof and it's——

ACT II (SAME EVENING)

The Kitchen of the Haycroft Farm

" You'll find us plain folk, sir, just plain folk. But if it'll please you to take what plain folk can offer you're heartily welcome. Now then, Phœbe girl, a chair here for the gentleman. Put another stick in the stove, Rube; it's a cold night in this November wind."

The stranger, in a strange voice, " Ay, it's a cold night."

The scene is in the farm kitchen, one of those big old farm kitchens of 1880 that filled the whole stage. There was a cooking-stove (about ten feet by six) off to the right side, and in the centre stage a fireplace with a mantle off at one side, and doors and windows—in fact, all the things that will be needed in the act, not forgetting a shot-gun hanging ominously on two hooks. At the back is a big table all laid out for about a dozen guests, with Phœbe, all done up in her best things, fussing round laying dishes. Martha Haycroft, also in her best things (black satin with a sort of crispiness to it), is cooking at the stove. Putting the farm people with their best clothes was always supposed to imply a comic touch. Rube has on clothes like a congressman's, only lower in the coat-tails and higher in the collar.

This, of course, was the supper that the farmer spoke of when he said they'd call in the neighbours.

Only for the moment all the eyes of the audience are turned on the stranger. He has a crop of straight white hair (a wig, evidently) and a white beard (false, of course), and he walks partly bent with a stick, and he looks all about him, all round the room, with such a queer look, as if he recognized it.

All the audience feel instinctively that that stranger is disguised. Indeed in this sort of play there always had to be somebody who turned out to be some one else.

" A raw night, sir," repeats the farmer, " there's an evil howl in the wind; I reckon there'll be stormy weather at sea to-night, sir——"

The farmer is evidently right—for just as he says it somebody behind the scene turns on the wind with a wild and mournful howl. Luckily they don't leave it on long, just enough to let the audience know it's there.

" I've just been down to the shore, sir," the farmer goes on. " I tend the light here at the foot of the farm. 'Twill be a bad night at sea to-night."

" A bad night for those at sea," repeats the stranger.

The wind howls again. Martha pauses in her cooking, looks a moment towards the window and murmurs, " The sea, the sea ! "

Martha, the farmer's wife, had to play alternately a pathetic character and a comic one. It was hard to do, but the audience understood it. So she mutters, " The sea, the sea ! " with the yearning of a mother for her lost son, and then goes back to blowing up pancakes on the cooking-stove. If that violated the unity of the drama we didn't know it in 1880, so it did no harm.

" But come, come," says the farmer, " this ain't no night for feeling down-hearted. I hear the neighbours outside. Come, Martha, we'll go out and bring them in."

This leaves Phœbe and Rube alone except for the stranger, who has gone across the room and is standing with his back to them, lost in thought. So Rube and Phœbe do another love scene. Rube comes to her alongside the table, and has only just time to say " Phœb ! " with a slow grin and to try

22

to take her by the waist, when she lands him across the face with a pancake. The audience roar with delight, and continue laughing till they suddenly come to a full stop when they see that there is something happening with the stranger.

He has been standing with his back turned, silent. Then, without warning, he speaks, his back still turned, not in his counterfeited tone, but in a loud clear voice, the voice of youth :

" Rube ! "

Rube and Phœbe start. " What voice is that ? " says Rube, shaking with agitation.

The stranger turns, plucks away his white wig and his white beard, and stands revealed.

" Jack ! It's Mr. Jack, come back from the dead ! " cries Phœbe.

" Ain't you drowned ? " cries Rube.

They crowd close to him in eager recognition ; and Jack, young and boyish now, laughs and greets them. " Let me run and call the boss and the missus," pleads Phœbe ; but Jack restrains her.

" Not now," he says, " they mustn't know yet."

He goes on to reveal, all in whispers and in gestures which the audience are not intended to unravel, that his father and mother must not know yet. He takes from his pocket a bundle of something—is it paper or money or what ? The audience can't see it decently, but Rube and Phœbe

23

seem to understand, and he is just explaining about it when the noise is heard of the farmer and his wife and the farm guests all coming back.

The stranger motions Rube and Phœbe to secrecy, and is disguised again in a minute.

In they all come, the farm people all dressed in the queer pathos of their Sunday things, and there follows the great supper scene, without which no rural melodrama was complete. Hear how they chatter and laugh. " Well, for the land's sake, taste them dough-nuts ! " " Neighbour Jephson, try a slice of this pie." " Well, I don't mind if I do." " Farmer Haycroft, here's your good health and Miss Hope's good health, and of all present." " Hear, hear ! " And then some one chokes on a crumb and is beaten on the back.

The supper scene lasts ten minutes by the clock. The stranger has sat silent, beaming quiet approval, and at the height of the merriment retired quietly to his room, a side-room opening on the kitchen. Martha has lighted a candle for him, and as he thanks her for it she says, " You're a stranger in these parts, sir ? There's something in your voice I seem to know."

All the audience want to shout, " He's your son." It is a touch taken right out of Sophocles. Hope meantime busies herself among the guests. Hiram Haycroft drinks great flagons of cider. At intervals the wind is turned on against the window panes to remind the audience that it's a wild night outside.

Then for a moment the farmer leaves the room because he has to go trim his light down on the shore.

While he is still out, there is loud knocking at the door. Rube goes to it and opens it—with a special biff of wind produced for his benefit—and then shows in two strangers, a young man and an old. The young man is tall and bronzed and sailorlike, and Hope runs to him at once, with a glad cry of " Ned ! My Ned ! "

His arms are about her in a moment, and the whole theatre knows that it is her husband.

" We've put in under the point," Ned explains, " and I came ashore. But it's only to say good-bye. The *Good Hope* can't lie there in this rising wind. We'll have to put off at once. This is my father, Hope. You'll be a daughter to him while I'm gone ! "

Hope goes up to the old man and puts her two hands in his, and says, oh so sweetly, " I will indeed, sir, for Ned's sake."

But her mother has risen, shrinking, from her place.

" Ellwood," she says, " Lawyer Ellwood."

All the audience look at the old man. A fox certainly—oh, a sly old fox—just that look of mean cunning that stamped every rural lawyer in every melodrama for thirty years. But Hope sees nothing of it.

"No, Ned, you mustn't put to sea to-night. It's too wild a night. Hear how the rain is driving at the windows. You must stay here, and your father too. Mother, this is Ned, my husband, and this is his father, and these are our friends, Ned, and father's only gone to the light. He'll be back in just a minute——"

And at that moment the door swings open and Hiram Haycroft—shaking the wet from his black oilskins—strides back into the room. Hope comes to him pleadingly.

"Father, father dear, this is my husband."

But he doesn't see her. He is staring at Ellwood.

"You!" he shouts. "You that have sought to bring ruin upon me and mine!"

Ellwood comes towards him, raising a protesting hand.

"Hiram!" he says.

"Out of my house!" shouts Haycroft. "Your accursed money is not due till to-morrow, and to-morrow it shall be paid. Out! before I lay hands on you." He steps forward menacingly, his hand uplifted.

Ned Ellwood steps in his way.

"Put down your hands," he says, "and listen to me."

26

Hiram refuses to listen. He reaches for the gun that hangs above the mantel. The affrighted guests crowd around him. There is noise and confusion, above which is Haycroft's voice, calling, " Out of my house ! I say."

The father and son move to the door, but as they go Hope rushes to her husband.

" Father ! He is my husband ! Where he goes I go. Ned, take me with you, out into the night and the storm." (At these words the wind, which has been quite quiet, breaks out again.) " Out into the world, for better or for worse. Where you go, I follow ; my place is at your side ! "

There is a burst of applause from the audience at this sentiment. That was the kind of girl they raised in 1880. There are none left now.

And so, with her father's imprecations ringing in her ears, Hope casts a little grey cloak over her head and shoulders, and with arm clinging to her husband passes out into the storm.

The door closes after them.

There is a hush and silence.

Not even Rube and Phœbe can break it now. The farm guests, almost inarticulate, come and say good night and pass out. Martha, lamp in hand, goes tearfully up the stairs. Rube and Phœbe fade away.

Hiram Haycroft sits alone. The lights are

dimmed down. There is a flicker of light from the fire in the stove, but little more. At times the rattle of the storm at the window makes him lift his head. Once he walks to the window and stands and gazes out into the darkness towards the sea.

And once he goes over to the dresser at the side of the room and takes from it the wallet that has in it his two thousand dollars, holds it a moment in his hand, and then replaces it.

At intervals the storm is heard outside. The audience by instinct know that the act is not over. There is more tragedy to come.

The farmer rises slowly from his chair. He lays aside his oilskins. Then, still slowly, he takes off his boot—with a bootjack—a stage effect much valued in melodrama.

He moves about the room, a candle in his hand, bolts and chains the door, and so, step by step, slowly and with much creaking, ascends the stairs to bed.

The audience follow in a breathless stillness. They know that something is going to happen.

Deep silence and waiting. You can hear the audience breathing. No one speaks.

Then a side door in the room is opened, slowly, cautiously. You can see a dark figure stealing across the stage—nearer and nearer to the drawer where the wallet of money is lying.   Look !   What is he doing ?   Is he taking it, or is he moving it ? Is it a thief, or what ?

Then suddenly the farmer's voice from above :

" Who's that down there ? "

You can half see the farmer as he stands on the upper landing, a candle in his hand.

" Who's that, I say ? " he calls again.

The crouching figure crawls away, making for the door.

What happens after that follows with a rush. The farmer comes hurrying down the stairs, tears open the drawer, and with a loud cry of " Thief ! A thief ! " rouses the sleeping house.   You hear the people moving above.   You see the lights on the stairs as the crouching figure rushes for the door. The farmer has seized his shot-gun.   There is a cry of " Stand there, or I'll shoot," then the flash of fire and the roar of the gun, and the crouching figure falls to the floor, the farmer shouting, " Lights here !   Bring a light !   A thief ! "

It is Rube who enters first, the others crowding after.   It is Rube who lifts the fallen body, Rube who holds the light on the pale face so that the audience may see who it is—but something has long since told them that.   It is Rube who pulls aside the white wig and the white beard that had disguised the youthful features.   There is a loud cry

from the farmer's wife as she sinks down beside the
body.

" Jack, Jack !   It's my boy come back to me ! "

And the farmer, the gun still clenched and smoking
in his hand, cries :

" My son !   I have killed my son ! "

And with that, down sinks the sombre curtain on
a silent audience.

. . . . .

That's the way, you see, that the drama was
put over in 1880.   We weren't afraid of real effects
—terror, agony, murder ; anything, and the more
of it the better.   In a modern drawing-room
play the characters get no nearer to murder
than to have *Pup No.* 1, dressed in grey tweeds,
discuss the theory of homicide with *Pup No.* 2,
dressed in a brown golf costume.   That's all
the excitement there is.   But in this good old
farm melodrama they weren't afraid of mixing
the thing up.

So the farmer is ruined, he's driven his daughter
from the door, and has shot his son—and there
you are.

When the play reaches this point, at the end
of Act II, there is nothing for it but a two years'
wait.   So the play-bill at this point bears the
legend, " Two Years elapse between Acts Two and
Three."

The audience are glad of it. Without that they couldn't have stood the tragedy of it. But, as it is, there are two years. The men rise and file out up the aisle; very slowly—there was no need to hurry with two years ahead of them.

The gas is turned up now and the audience are gradually recovering; a boy comes down the aisles and shouts "Pea-nuts!" That helps a lot. And presently, when the orchestra begins to play "Little Annie Rooney is my Sweetheart," they begin to get reconciled to life again. Anyway, being used to this type of play, they know that things aren't so bad as they seem. Jack can't really be dead. He'll be brought to life somehow. He was shot, but he can't have been killed. Every audience knows its own line of play; in fact, in all the drama the audience has to be taken for granted or the play wouldn't be intelligible. Anybody who has seen a moving-picture audience snap up the symbols and legends and conventions of a photo-play and get the required meaning out of it will know just what I mean. So it was in 1880. The audience got cheered up because they realized that Jack couldn't really be dead.

So they look at their programmes with a revived interest to see what happens next.

Here it is:

ACT III (TWO YEARS LATER)

The Foreshore after Sunset—A Gathering Storm

Ah! Look at the scene as the curtain goes up now. Isn't it grand? The rocks and the breaking water and the white foam in the twilight! How ever do they do it? And the lighthouse there at the right-hand side, how it towers into the dark sky! Look at the fishermen all in black oilskins and sou'westers, glistening in the wet, moving about on the shore and pointing to the sea.

Notice that short flash of yellow lightning and the rumble of thunder away behind the scene. And look at the long beams of the light from the lighthouse far out on the water.

Don't talk to me of a problem play, played in a modern drawing-room as between a man in tweed and a woman in sequins. When I attend the theatre let there be a lighthouse and a gathering of huddled fishermen, and danger lowering over the sea. As drama it is worth all the sex stuff that was ever slopped over the footlights.

" A wild night ! "

It's a fisherman speaking—or no, it's Rube, only you would hardly know him—all in oilskins. In the New England play all the farmers turn into

fishermen as the plot thickens. So it is Zeke, as
another fisherman, who answers :

"It's all that. God help all poor souls out at
sea to-night!"

The lightning and thunder make good again,
the fishermen and the women on the shore move
to and fro, talking, and excited, and pointing at the
sea. Rube and Zeke come together in the fore-
ground, talking. Their function is to let the
audience know all that has happened in two years.

"A wild night," Zeke repeats, "such a night
as it was two years ago, you mind, the night that
Mr. Jack was shot."

They both shake their heads. "'Twould have
been a sight better," says Rube, "if the farmer's
bullet had killed him that night. A sad sight it
is to see him as he is, witless and speechless. It's
cruel hard on them all. Is he here to-night?"

"Ay, he's here to-night—he's always here on
the shore when a storm is on. Look, see him there,
always looking to the sea!"

The audience look at once, and see, in the little
group standing in the gathering storm, Jack,
holding to his mother hard and looking out to sea.

"She's leading him away. She'll be wanting
him to go home. . . ."

So Jack isn't dead! But what is that queer,
strange look on his face? Something blank, un-

human, witless. His mother leads him down the stage.

"Jack! come home, Jack! It's no place for you here in the storm."

The thunder and lightning break in again sharp and vivid, and the wind roars behind the scenes.

Jack turns a vacant countenance upon his mother. His face is pale and thin. His eyes are bright.

The audience get it. Since he was shot down he has been there two years, speechless and demented.

His mother keeps begging him to come home. He tries to drag her towards the sea. Demented as he is, there is a wild and growing excitement in his manner. He is pointing at the waves, gesticulating.

"What does he see?" Rube is asking. "What is it? He has a sailor's eyes. What does he see out there?"

And at that minute there comes a shout from the clustered fishermen on the foreshore:

"A ship! A ship! There's a vessel out on the reef. See! Look!"

They run up and down, pointing and shouting. And far out on the waves, lit for a moment by a flash of lightning, the audience sees a dismasted schooner—she's made of cardboard—out beside the breakers of the reef.

At this moment the freckled boy, all in oilskins,

rushes breathless on to the stage. He hasn't grown an inch in two years, but nobody cares about that.

" Mother! Rube! " he gasps. " I've been down to the Long Point—I ran all the way—there is a schooner going on the reef. Look, you can see, and, mother, mother——"

The boy is almost frenzied into excitement. The crowd gathers about him.

" Mother, it's the *Good Hope*, her ship ! "

" The *Good Hope* ! " exclaims everybody.

The boy gasps on.

" They were lowering the boats—I could see them—but nothing can live in that sea—one boat went down—I saw it—and I could see her, Hope, standing by the mast. I could see her face when the lightning came. Then I ran here. We must go out ; we must get the life-boats ; we've got to go. You men, who'll come ? "

Come ? They'll all come ! Listen to the shout of them. See ! they are dragging forth the life-boat from its wooden house on the left of the stage. There are swinging lanterns and loud calls and the roaring of the wind. The stage is darkening and the lightning glares on the sea. But even as they are trying to launch the life-boat, there's a new cry :

" Look ! A boat ! a boat ! out there on the reef, right among the breakers ! "

The fishermen rush up and down in great excitement. " There's a woman in the boat ! God help her ! She's lost ! "

" Mother, mother, it's Hope ! See, she's alone in the boat; she's kneeling up ; she's praying."

There are new cries :

" Man the life-boat ! Man the life-boat ! "

The great boat is dragged out and ready. The men are climbing in over the side.

Then a fisherman shouts out and is heard, clear and single, for a moment in the lull of the storm.

" There's only one man can pilot this boat across that reef, only Hiram Haycroft."

There are cries of " Hiram ! Hiram ! " They point out at the lighthouse from which the long beams still revolve on the water. " He can't leave the light."

Noise and commotion.

" He must leave the light."

" It's life or death on this one chance. Lads, stand ready there with the life-boat, and come some of you with me and bring him down." They rush towards the lighthouse. There is noise and thunder ; a flash of light shows the boat, clearly in sight now, right out among the breakers, and Hope seen for a moment, kneeling in the bow praying, her face illuminated in the lightning. Then, in a swirl of white water, the boat vanishes in the foam of the reef.

36

Act IV

Then the scene changes—all done in a minute—from the shore to the "Lighthouse Tower." It was what used to be called a "transformation scene." It involved an eclipse of darkness punctured by little gas jets, and a terrible thumping and bumping with an undertone of curses. You could hear a voice in the darkness say quite distinctly, "Get that blank blank drop over there," and you could see black figures running round in the transformation. Then there came an awful crash and a vision of a back curtain sliding down amongst the dark men. The lights flicked up again, and all the audience broke into applause at the final wonder of it.

Look! It's the lighthouse tower with the big lights burning and the storm howling outside. How bright and clear it is here inside the tower, with its great windows looking out over the storm sixty feet above the sea.

He stands beside the lights, trimming the lamps, calm and steady at his task. The storm is all about him, but inside the lighthouse tower all is bright and still.

Hiram peers a moment from the lighthouse window. He opens the little door and steps out on the iron platform high above the sea. The

37

wind roars about him and the crest of the driven water leaps to his very feet. He comes in, closing the door quietly and firmly behind him, and turns again to his light.

" God help all poor souls at sea to-night ! " he says.

And then with a rush and clatter of feet they burst in upon him, the group of fishermen, Martha, and his demented son, crowding into the lighthouse tower and standing on the stairs. Jack is at the rear of all, but there is a strange look on his face, a light of new intelligence.

" Quick, Hiram, you must come ! There's been a wreck. Look, there's a boat going on the reef. The men are ready in the life-boat. You must steer her through. It's life or death. There's not a moment to lose."

Hiram looks for a moment at the excited crowd and then turns quietly to his task.

" My place is here," he says.

There is a moment's hush. Martha rushes to him and clutches him by the coat.

" Hiram, they haven't told you. The schooner that was wrecked to-night is the *Good Hope*."

Hiram staggers back against the wall.

" And the boat that's drifting on the reef, it's Hope; it's our daughter ! "

Hiram stands grasping the rail along the wall. He speaks, panting with agitation, but firm :

38

" Martha—I'm sworn to tend the light. If the light fails, God knows what it means to the ships at sea. If my child is lost, it is God's will—but—my place is here."

And he turns back to the light.

The fishermen, who have been crowding close to the window, cry :

" Look down below ! The boat—she's driving in here right on the rocks—the woman still clinging to her ! "

Martha rushes to the window and calls : " My child ! save my child ! save her ! " And at exactly this minute Jack steps out into the centre of the floor. His face is clear and plain beneath the light.

" Father ! " he says. " Mother ! "

They all turn to look at him. But no one speaks.

" The rope," he says ; " give me the rope."

He points to a long coil of rope that hangs against the wall.

In a moment, with the end of the line around his body, Jack has thrown open the door and rushed on to the little iron platform. He pauses there for a second and then the audience see him mount upon the iron rail and then dive, head first, into the sea below.

There is shouting and clamour from the fisher-men. " There he is ! He's swimming to her !

Hold fast the line there ! He's got her ! Now then, all together on the line ! "

And with one glorious haul up comes the line from the roaring sea, with Jack at the end of it, and, fast held in his encircling arm, the fainting form of his sister.

Couldn't be done ? Nonsense. That was nothing to what we used to see in the old-time plays. If need be, Jack could have fished up a whole shipload.

There is a cry of " Saved ! Saved ! " and Hiram Haycroft, clasping the senseless form of his daughter to his heart, cries :

" My little gal ! Cast up by the sea ! " and down comes the curtain in a roar of applause.

ACT V (SIX MONTHS LATER)

Scene. The Kitchen of the Haycroft Farm

This last act in the melodrama is all to the good. There is no more tragedy, no strain, no trouble. The play is really over, but this part is always put in as a sort of wind-up to make everybody happy. The audience are now sitting in a swim of luxurious sentimentality. How fine everything has turned out—Jack has got his mind back, and Hope is saved, and her husband too, and the old farm isn't mort-gaged or sold, and the Haycrofts are not ruined after all. Yes, and more than that : there are all kinds of little items of happiness to be thrown in.

So here we are back in the old farm kitchen, and here, of course, are Rube and Phœbe again. And Rube tries to grab Phœbe round the waist, but she says, " Oh, you Rube, you go along," and lands a dish-cloth in his face. But this time Rube *won't* go along. He manages to catch Phœbe and tell her that he wants her to be his wife, and to throw dish-cloths at him all his life ; and Phœbe calls him a " big thing," and gives him a kiss like a smack (worse than a dish-cloth or a pancake). So there they are all set for marriage, as they might have been in the first act if Rube had had the nerve.

Well, they are no sooner straightened out than in come the farmer and his son Jack, and Ned, Hope's husband. The farmer seems very old and infirm, though suffused with the same air of peace and happiness as all the others. The two young men help him into an arm rocking-chair. . . . " Easy now." Then Hiram sits down with that expression of difficulty, " Ay-ee-ee," always used to symbolize stage rheumatism. There is no need for the farmer to become so suddenly old in the last act. But it was a favourite convention of 1880 to make all the old people very infirm and very happy at the end of the play.

So they begin to talk, just to pile on the happiness.

" I'm getting old, lads ; I'm not the man I was."

" Old, father ? " laughs Jack, " why, you're the youngest and spryest of all of us——"

" I'm getting past work, boys," says the farmer, shaking his head, " past work——"

" Work," says Jack, " why should you work ? " And as the talk goes on you get to understand that Jack will never go to sea again, but will stay and work the farm, and they've just received the " papers " that appoint him keeper of the light in his father's place, with a pension for the old man. And Ned, Hope's husband, is going to stay right there too. His father has bought him the farm just adjoining, with house and stock and everything, and he and Hope are all ready to move into it just as soon as——

But wait a minute.

His father ! Lawyer Ellwood ! And the terrible enmity and feud !

Oh, pshaw ! just watch that feud vanish. In the fifth act of an old-time melodrama a feud could be blown to the four winds like thistledown.

Like this :

There's a knocking at the door, and Ned goes to it, and comes back all smiling, and he says :

" There's some one at the door to see you, Mr. Haycroft. An old friend, he says. Shall he come in ? "

"An old friend?" And in slips Ellwood—the farmer's enemy, Hope's father-in-law — looking pretty hale and hearty, but with the same touch of the old age of the fifth act visible.

He comes over and says:

"Well, Hiram, have you a shake of the hand for an old friend?"

And the farmer, rising, unsteadily:

"Why, Ephraim, it's not your hand I should be taking; it's your forgiveness I ought to ask, for my mad folly these two years past."

"Forgiveness?" says the lawyer. How honest and cheery he looks now, not a bit like the scoundrel he seemed in the second act. "Forgiveness!"

And off he goes with *his* explanation.

What's the whole purpose of the fifth act—explanation!

And what do you think! He'd been Hiram's friend all along, and was not in earnest about wanting the money back from Hiram—didn't want it at all! And he knew all about Hope's love affair and Jack's safe return with his son, and was tickled to death over it—and that night two years ago, when the farmer drove him out, he had come over to tell the Haycrofts that the debt was cancelled, and he was going to buy a farm and start the young people, Ned and Hope, in life—and it was the cancelled mortgage that Jack was trying to sneak over and put in the drawer when his father shot him down !—and—why, dear me, how simple it all is in the fifth act. Why didn't he explain ? Why didn't he shout out, " Hiram, I'm not a villain at all ; I'm your old friend ! " Oh, pshaw ! who ever did *explain* things in the second act of a melodrama ? And where would the drama be if they did ?

So they are still explaining and counter-explaining and getting happier and happier when the last climax is staged.

The audience hear Martha's voice as she comes on to the stage, talking back into the wings, " Carry him carefully there, Phœbe, for the land's sake. If you drop that precious child——"

And in they come.

Martha and Hope ! Looking as sweet and fresh as when she started out years ago in the first act. And bringing up the rear, Phœbe—*carrying the Baby !*

Yes, believe it or not, a baby !—or the very semblance of one all bundled up in white.

Hope's baby !

No melodrama was ever brought to its righteous end without a baby.

How the women all cuddle round it and croon over it ! They put it on the farmer's lap—and, say, isn't he just clumsy when he tries to take it ?—and when Rube offers to help, and Phœbe slaps his face with a dish-rag, the audience just go into paroxysms of laughter.

So there you are—and everybody saved. All happy, the baby installed on the farmer's knees, and explanations flowing like autumn cider.

All that is needed now is the farmer to get off the *Final Religious Sentiment*, which is the end and benediction of the good old melodrama. So he utters it with all due solemnity : " Ay, lads, pin your hope in Providence, and in the end you land safe in front."

It sounds as convincing as a proposition in Euclid. Then the curtain slowly comes down and the *matinée* audience melts away, out into the murky November evening, with the flickering gas lamps in the street, and the clinging bells of the old horse-cars in their ears, but with their souls uplifted and illuminated with the moral glow of the melodrama.

II—"Dead Men's Gold," a Film of the Great Nevada Desert

A FILM of the great Nevada Desert, in which Red-Blooded, Able-Bodied Men and Women, a hundred per cent American, live and love among the cactus and chaparral. Something of the Ozone of the Cow Pasture mingled with the Gloom of the Great Cañons blows all through this Play.

Shall we go together this raw gusty afternoon to the enchantment of the Moving Pictures? Here, this looks a good place, this large and lighted hall leading off the street itself. Let's get our tickets from this Golden Girl behind the glass, seated there under a magic spell, no doubt. This *must* be a good play; look how pretty the girl is! Two, yes please, downstairs—extra ten cents? Oh, the Amusement Tax of course!

Now through these doors and down this corridor, and through these swinging doors again and into the dark. What a vast place it is! Dear me, it's absolutely empty! Empty? Oh no, they are all

46

there, but you don't see them yet, seated silent in
the dark, like toads under leaves. Excuse me, sir,
I'm afraid I stepped on your foot. I beg your
pardon, madam, I didn't see the little girl.

All that bright picture stuff being flashed on the
screen ? Never mind it now till we get our seats.
It's not part of our play anyhow. There, sit down
in this row—now we can look—what does it say ?—
TURKISH TROOPS ENTER THE—something—I couldn't
see—anyway, it doesn't matter where they enter, it's
only the News of the World. PASADENA CALIFORNIA
PRESIDENT HARDING PRESENTS FLOWERS TO GIRL
GUIDES STATE UNIVERSITY OF OHIO DEFEATS MIAMI AT
BASKET-BALL NATIVES OF DUTCH PAPUA HUNTING
FROGS PRINCE ARTHUR IN WESTMINSTER ABBEY CATCH-
ING TARPON : Oh, don't let us bother with all this,
the pictures haven't begun yet !

Ah, now it's going to begin ! Look at that
notice on the screen :

DEAD MEN'S GOLD IN WHICH FULL-BLOODED
MEN AND WOMEN LIVE AND LOVE AMONG
THE CACTUS AND CHAPARRAL AUTHORIZED
BY THE CENSOR OF NEW YORK STATE

That sounds interesting, doesn't it ? Let's see
what's put up next. Ah, a great face, a huge
face under a cowboy hat, a face with a grin on it ;
yes, that's him, see, it says so underneath :

BIG-HEARTED JIM SHERIFF OF DEAD BONES COUNTY NEVADA

See him turn his face round as he grins. My! how honest and attractive the human face looks when you make it four feet long. I wish they'd put it upside down. I think it would look even better. Now, what's this next—ah—

BESSEMER STEEL, BANKER, OF NEW YORK

—very rich indeed, evidently. How do I know that?—Oh, pshaw! you don't understand Moving Pictures—look at his grey spats and that white frill along his waistcoat—that means a millionaire. No, no, this isn't the play yet; these are only the people who are going to be in the play when it starts. Ah, *now* look!

MAISIE, BESSEMER STEEL'S ONLY DAUGHTER

Isn't she just cute? See her smile, no wonder they applaud her—and who is this?

DANN YEGG, BAD MAN OF DEAD MEN'S GULCH

Bad, well I should say so! And now, see all these little scenes going rapidly past—well, they're not the play yet—those are merely places that are

48

going to be *in* the play—just little touches of lonely desert, and terrible caverns, and a dear little vignette of a man choking another in a cave—and a pretty little wee glimpse of a man dying of thirst—just little foretastes of the play itself. It looks good stuff, doesn't it ? Now, we're off !

BESSEMER STEEL OF NEW YORK, BANKER AND FINANCIER, HAS SPENT HIS LIFE IN THE AMASSING OF MILLIONS

There he is in his office : see all the desks and stenographers round him. What a big, dull face he has ; like a bullfrog you say ? Yes, all New York bankers have faces like that in the Movies. See him speaking into his desk telephone. Say, isn't he authoritative ? Now, look, he's listening. Must be about money from the way he shuts up his face. I guess he's refusing somebody one of those millions that he's amassed. Now he's signing a cheque. Now he's receiving a telegram. . . . In fact, by this time I think we've quite grasped the idea that he's a rich banker with no soul. In fact, I think I could have grasped it a little sooner, couldn't you ? But, still, remember the Moving Pictures have to be made clear to the humblest intelligence. And that isn't us. . . . Aha ! no *soul* did we say ?—Look at this :

THE ONLY TENDER SPOT IN THE BANKER'S
HEART IS FOR HIS DAUGHTER MAISIE. TO
HER HE DENIES NOTHING

See, the pictures are about to establish the fact
that Maisie is denied nothing. Look at her there
in her palatial home, romping with a pet dog. Oh,
how sweet she is! See her kiss that dog—oh, my!
I wonder what they pay that dog for its part.
There she is, riding her pony round the grounds;
now she is entertaining a whole bevy of her girl
friends on the lawn; now she's in a store buying
rich things—say, I think it's proved up to the
hilt that that girl is denied nothing. On with the
film—but wait—just a minute—did you notice
among the clerks in the office that young man . . .
sort of Spanish-looking, mean-looking—kind of
a crook—species of skunk—evidently *not* a hundred
per cent American—in fact, hardly twenty per
cent? See the way he keeps a sort of furtive eye
on the banker? Say, I believe that fellow must
come into the play somehow—just watch him.
Never mind, he's gone, but he'll come in again.
Now we go on. Ah, this is more like:

ASCOT WRIGHT, STUDENT AT HARVARD

I'm glad it's Harvard. So much more class to
it than the Ontario Agricultural College——

HAS DISCOVERED IN HIS RESEARCHES IN THE
HARVARD LIBRARY THE LOCATION OF A LOST
GOLD MINE IN A CAVERN IN DEAD MEN'S
GULCH NEAR GRAVEYARD CAÑON IN DEAD
BONES COUNTY NEVADA

Here we have him, Ascot Wright researching in
the library, the way all Harvard students do.
How neat he is! I thought all researchers looked
pretty dusty, but perhaps not. Anyhow, Ascot
is as neat as a pin, and athletic-looking, and awfully
well dressed for a student. Perhaps his father is
a Harvard professor. Now see! Evidently he's
struck something among the books—see him take
paper from the leaves of an old volume! He's
examining it—feverishly—say, I can just tell that
Ascot has discovered a gold mine. He's working
his face just the way a student does when he finds
one. Ah, see that! You don't understand?
Those pictures represent what Ascot is reading
about. Look, that's the Great Western Desert.
. . . See the little troop of people, horsemen and
mules with pack-saddles, crossing it; see the steel
uniforms and breastplates and swords — early
Spaniards, that's what they are, the first discoverers
of the West. . . . Look, they've entered a cavern—
oh, say! the gloom of it! They're digging with
pickaxes! Look, look! They're piling up great

bars of gold. They're mad with excitement—
they're quarrelling — they're fighting — they're
stabbing one another. . . . Look, dead bodies—
dead bones—dead bones in the cavern—dead bones
all along the trail—it means the survivors tried to
escape, do you see ? Look, here's one, he's the
last . . . he's dying of thirst in the desert ; see him
writing on a bit of paper . . . there, he's folded
it into a missal, a prayer book or something. I
know what it is—it's the description of all about
the mine in the cavern, and the piled-up gold, do
you see, and that's the paper that Ascot Wright
has found in the Harvard library three hundred
years later. Look, it's saying so :

THE MANUSCRIPT WRITTEN IN LATIN BY
THE DYING SPANISH EXPLORER PEDRO AL-
VAREZ DE ESTORGA IS DECIPHERED BY THE
HARVARD STUDENT

There's Ascot ; look at him with the paper in
front of him, deciphering it !—deciphering *Latin* !
Isn't he a bird ? My ! A Harvard education is
a wonderful thing ! Now, what's it saying ?

THE HARVARD STUDENT LAYS HIS DISCOVERY
BEFORE THE GREAT FINANCIER

There he is, that's Ascot in Bessemer Steel's inner
office. How neat he looks in his covert coat and

his hard hat ! These Harvard students certainly have class. He's explaining to the banker all about the mine. . . . The great banker is listening. . . . He's hearing all about the documents. . . . See the pictures go by again—desert—cavern— bones—more bones—dying Spaniard—document— bones—gold. . . . He's got it ! These New York bankers are just lightning at picking up bones and gold.

Now he's speaking :

MR. WRIGHT, THIS MUST BE KEPT A PROFOUND
SECRET

Oh, but can it be ? Look who's listening . . . that clerk, you remember the crook, the one with the cunning face; he's pushed open the door a little way. He's standing listening—they don't see him.

. . . . WE WILL GO WEST AT ONCE. I WILL
DEFRAY THE EXPENSES OF THE SEARCH AND
DIVIDE WITH YOU FIFTY-FIFTY

What splendid English those great bankers use ! So clear, isn't it ?

And, just then, who comes dancing into the office through the side door ? Maisie. Isn't she just sweet with her fur round her neck ? say look, she's got one of those new skirts. Watch her go and throw her arms around the banker's neck.

See his face light up! In fact, you can see him light it up. Now he is introducing Ascot Wright to Maisie. They bow to each other—say, Ascot is taken with Maisie right away, isn't he? Now the Spanish clerk comes in with papers in his hands. He bows to Maisie. How coldly she nods to him! But look at his eyes when he looks at her. I get it, don't you? And that look of hate which he hands to Ascot. Those Spaniards certainly have temperament—the moving pictures would be lost without them.

Now the banker is speaking:

MR. GONZALEZ, I AM LEAVING TO-NIGHT FOR NEVADA. WILL YOU KINDLY MAKE THE ARRANGEMENTS FOR MY TRANSPORTATION . . .

Look, Maisie wants to go too. She's questioning her father . . . he's shaking his head . . . she's put her arms around his neck. Oh, take her, take her, or I'll buy a ticket to Nevada and take her myself.

Scene changed. The Pennsylvania Station. Look at all the people. Isn't it just wonderful to see the Pennsylvania Station in the moving pictures? Much better than in real life; but, then, so's everything. They're leaving for Nevada. Maisie is going too; there she is: do you notice she's got on one of those new coats they're wearing?

Do you like them ? And there's Ascot. That's
a nice valise he has . . . and the banker, and
Gonzalez. No, he's not going, he's just seeing
them off. The banker's giving him papers and
instructions . . . there, they're getting on their
journey. See the landscape flying past — now
they're in a dining-car. See the darky waiters—
look at the banker ordering lunch. I'll bet he
knows how. He'll eat lunch all the way to Nevada.

But look — we're back at the station. It's
Gonzalez, he's buying a ticket. He's getting on
the train. . . . I see it, don't you ? He's following
them. I knew he would.

Now the scene has changed altogether. They're
arriving in Nevada. This is Cañon City. . . .
What a queer empty spot ! . . . shack houses and
desert and hills all around it. . . . See the wooden
hotel, with the veranda and the men on horseback
with leather trousers and with lariats on the pommel
of the saddle, and the men leaning against the
veranda posts with lariats slung over their arms.
Look at that big man with the slouch hat and
the wide face ! That's the one it showed at the
beginning. He's Big Jim, the Sheriff . . . he's talking to them . . . they're explaining what they want.

Now it's changed again. Where is this place ?—
Oh yes, I recognize it—it's a saloon—see the bar
and all the bottles and the bartender leaning over

it—pretty tough-looking, isn't it ? . . . see the men sitting at the little table drinking whisky. . . . I've seen this sort of place a hundred times in the movies, haven't you ? It's always called Pete's Place or something like that. . . . That's Gonzalez, one of the men drinking, and that other is Dan Yegg, the bad man that we saw, and the rest, I guess, are bandits . . . they must be. . . . Now, Gonzalez is explaining. He's telling about Bessemer Steel and Ascot Wright coming to hunt for the gold . . . he's telling the story of the Spanish explorers. . . . There it goes—desert, bones, gold, more bones, dying Spaniard. They've got it. Look how excited they get.

Now it's changed back to Ascot and his friends. . . . They're mounting on horseback. Doesn't Maisie look nice in that short skirt ? I guess she brought it with her on purpose. Look at the armed men, quite a troop of them. Oh, I guess they'd need them in a place like that. . . . Big Jim is pointing and giving advice ; I suppose he's telling them the way to Dead Men's Gulch. There, they're off, clattering out of the town and away.

SEPARATED FROM THEIR ARMED ESCORT, ASCOT AND HIS COMPANIONS MAKE THEIR WAY INTO THE HEART OF DEAD MEN'S GULCH

Separated from their armed escort? A crazy thing to do in a place like that, you say? Oh, yes, but they always do it, in all the romances. The first thing you have to do with an armed escort is to separate yourself from it.

But say, look at the Gulch. Isn't that the gloom spot? See the great walls of rock towering above their heads, and the litter of boulders, where they pick their way. Look, that's a snake, a real snake! Ugh! Aren't they crazy to go into a place like that? There's Ascot leading them—with a little bit of map or chart in his hand. And, oh, look, look! Do you see that? Those heads behind the rocks, they're being followed—it's Gonzalez and Dan Yegg and Mexican bandits. Say, it's just madness to get separated from that escort.

What's this? They've stopped. Ascot's pointing. He's found the entrance of a sort of tunnel into the cliff . . . they're going into it. . . . They're carrying flashlights. . . . The light shines on the rock walls. . . . What a fearsome place! . . . Look, written there on the wall in strange lettering:

PEDRO ALVAREZ DE ESTORGA

1 6 2 1

They gather round it. . . . They're reading the inscription. . . . Now they're going on. The tunnel is widening—it's opening into a great

cavern . . . notice the high ceiling and the hanging
rocks with the water dripping from them. . . .
I suppose it's dripped like that for centuries—see
the floor all sand—and there ! bones of dead men,
and a steel breastplate and part of a broken sword,
and over in the corner gold piled up in bars, and
great nuggets of it heaped up—on the floor.

Ascot is picking up the gold and showing it to
Maisie. Bessemer Steel has taken up a nugget
and is examining it. I bet he knows to a fraction
what it is worth. Ha ! He's showing it and
speaking :

I ESTIMATE THAT THERE IS AT A CONSERVA-
TIVE ESTIMATE TWO MILLION DOLLARS OF
GOLD LYING AT OUR FEET

Say ! Two million ! and at a conservative estimate ! Think of the coolness of the man making
a conservative estimate in a place like that.

Great heavens ! The whole three of them
have turned in sharp alarm ! They hear something—some one in the tunnel. Here they come
dashing into the cavern—armed men—Gonzalez
and Yegg and the bandits. They've rushed at
Ascot and the banker . . . three of them are
fighting Ascot all at once . . . go to it, Ascot,
that's the way. Now he's down—no, he's up again—
he's down—they're clubbing him—and the banker,

Dan Yegg has him down and is choking him. That's the way, choke him—keep it up. Now this is really enjoyable. This is the real thing . . . go on—keep on choking him . . . that's right, pound Ascot over the head with a rock—admirable— I do like these choking scenes, don't you ?

They're both insensible—inanimate on the floor of the cave—now they've grabbed Maisie—they're binding her with cords—good . . . twist her up tight—that's the way. Give her another wind. It enhances the educational value of the film.

There, they've gathered her up . . . they've put the gold into bags . . . they're carrying Maisie and the gold down the tunnel . . . they're coming out at the entrance. Oh, see what they're doing . . . they're blocking the mouth of the tunnel with great rocks . . . the bodies of Ascot and Bessemer will never be found.

Now they're lifting Maisie into a motor-car . . . that must have been waiting down the gulch . . . they've got her mouth gagged ; I hadn't noticed that before. That's a good touch, isn't it ? . . . There, they're all in . . . they're off . . . out of the gulch . . . out on the mesa . . . away . . . away . . . fading into the distant hills . . . gone.

Where is it now ? It's such a poor light, I can't see, can you ? Oh, yes, I get it. It's inside the cave again. . . . Ascot and Bessemer Steel flat on the sand . . . the light is that electric torch still lying on its side and burning. . . . Look, Ascot moved his arm . . . he's reviving . . . he's half sitting up . . . he's feeling Bessemer Steel's heart. Bessemer's reviving too. They'll both be all right in a few minutes. They were only clubbed with rocks and stabbed and choked. That's nothing. Movie actors go through far worse than that and revive. . . . Didn't I tell you . . . Ascot has stood up . . . he walks painfully . . . for five seconds . . . now he walks all right . . . he's looking round . . . he's taking the torch and going into the tunnel . . . he's coming back . . . he's speaking to Bessemer :

THEY HAVE WALLED UP THE MOUTH OF THE
TUNNEL

Yes, Ascot, we knew that, we saw them doing it. But look at the horror on Bessemer Steel's face . . . now he's speaking :

ASCOT, WE ARE LOST. THERE IS NOTHING
IN FRONT OF US BUT A SLOW DEATH

But look at Ascot . . . see his set jaw and his clenched hand and his brave face ; see what he says :

WE ARE NOT LOST MR. STEEL. I CAN SAVE
US YET

Oh, bully for you, Ascot, that's the stuff! That Harvard training does it every time.

What ever is Ascot doing now? . . . He's picking up the broken bits of the old Spanish armour . . . he's fitting things together. . . . What's he making? He's taken out a long thin wire from his pocket, a coil of it . . . he's fastened a weight to it, he's thrown it to the roof of the cave . . . it's caught on a jag of rock . . . now's he's fastening it down tight on the ground and attaching something to it. Ah, I catch on, I see it, don't you? Why, radio! He's got a radio machine with him; now they'll make it all clear in writing in a minute—didn't I tell you? There it is:

ASCOT WRIGHT WITH THE AID OF A WIRE
AND THE FRAGMENTS OF OLD ARMOUR AND
AN ELECTRIC TORCH MAKES A RADIO
" MR. STEEL IN FIVE MINUTES I SHALL BE IN
COMMUNICATION WITH CAÑON CITY "

Look! He's getting into communication . . . zik—zik—see the big blue sparks running down the wire and lighting up the cave . . . zik—zak—zak—zak—zik . . . he's sending his message.

Ah! Here's the other end of it. The wireless station at Cañon City. See the operator in his room, with a sort of helmet on, and the wires and sparks all round him . . . zik—zak—zik . . . the

message is coming through.   Look at the operator
—all hurry and alarm, he writes down the message
. . . he's dashed out with it in his hand . . . he's
reading it to Big Jim, the Sheriff.   See the excited
crowd gathering.   Jim's haranguing them.

MR. STEEL AND ASCOT WRIGHT ARE WALLED
UP IN A CAVE OFF DEAD MEN'S GULCH.   MISS
STEEL HAS BEEN CARRIED OFF BY BANDITS.
I WANT EVERY MAN THAT CAN RIDE AND
HANDLE A GUN

Hurrah !   That's the way—off they go.   See them
leap on the horses and off in a whirl of dust . . . see
the Winchester rifles slung over their shoulders . . .
there's Big Jim at the head of them . . . out
of the town and over the desert. . . . There,
they're riding into the Gulch . . . Ascot must
have given them the directions . . . they've
halted . . . they're at the walled-up tunnel . . .
they're tearing down the stones . . . they're entering the cave . . . it's bright now with torches . . .
and crowded with men . . . they've found Ascot
and Bessemer Steel. . . . Big Jim has put a flask
to their lips . . . that'll help them. . . . Now
Ascot's explaining, the gold, the attack, everything. . . . See the crowd listening with the light
on their faces !

   Out of the cave . . . out into the bright sunshine . . . and riding, riding for life . . . but where ? How can they know ? . . . and the motor had a long start. What is that they plan to do ? . . . riding, riding, they don't seem to be chasing anything, they seem to be going somewhere. Oh, look, what is this place with tall frame sheds and the level ground ?—oh ! I get it—fine ! fine ! See that great sign :

AEROPLANE STATION OF THE GOVERNMENT
OF THE UNITED STATES

Isn't that great ? What a thing it is to live under a government that keeps aeroplanes even away out in the desert.

Now they're running an aeroplane out of the shed—what a huge machine. They're getting in, Bessemer Steel, and Big Jim, the Sheriff, and his men. See, Ascot is going to steer ; I guess his head is all right again now. That little thumping with the rocks merely woke up his brain.

Away they go—up—up—see the machine soaring in the blue sky, floating, hovering like a great bird watching for its prey . . . it's circling round searching for the motor-car. Aha ! they must see it now. Look at the aeroplane swooping down . . . and see, there's the motor . . . rushing over the mesa . . . here it's coming right past us. Gonzalez is at the wheel. There's Maisie in the back of the car still tied . . . here's the aeroplane right after it . . . look at Dan Yegg standing up in the car and shooting at the aeroplane with a revolver. . . . They're shooting back . . . that's Big Jim with his Winchester, leaning over the edge of the car . . . look at the motor running straight for the edge of the cañon. . . . Great Cæsar! it's gone over . . . it's a drop of a thousand feet . . . look . . . there's the car falling through the air, the wheels still spinning . . . and there's the aeroplane chasing it as it falls. . . . Watch Big Jim . . . he's got a coil of rope, a lasso . . . he's lassoed Maisie with it. . . . Hurrah! they're hauling her on to the aeroplane. . . . The motor can fall now, it doesn't matter where it falls to. . . . There's the aeroplane landed . . . Maisie's unbound . . . she's in her father's arms . . . he's handing her to Ascot. . . .

What's it saying?—Oh, that's just the wind-up:

AND SO THESE TWIN SOULS JOIN HENCEFORTH
TO WALK LIFE'S PATHWAY HAND IN HAND
NEXT WEEK MUTT AND JEFF AMONG THE
MONKEYS DON'T MISS IT

III—"*The Soul Call*," an Up-to-Date Piffle-Play. Period 1923

(*In which a Woman and a Man, both trying to find themselves, find each other*)

A T the opposite pole of thought from the good old melodrama, full of wind and seaweed and danger, is the ultra-modern, up-to-date Piffle-Play.

It is named by such a name as *The Soul Call*, or *The Heart Yearn*, or *The Stomach Trouble*— always something terribly perplexed and with 60 per cent of sex in it. It always deals in one way or another with the "problem of marriage." Let it be noted that marriage, which used to be a sacrament, became presently a contract and now a problem. In art and literature it used to constitute the happy ending. Now it's just the bad beginning.

You always hear of *The Soul Call* long before you see it. It is being played in London before New York, or in New York before London, or at any rate it is always played somewhere else first. It has to be. That's part of the charm of it. So that you have heard people discussing it at dinner, and debating whether Helga was right in wanting to poison her husband, and how Lionel Derwent could live with such a woman as Mabel.

When at last it is played it is put on in a Little Theatre, just a small bijou place, with seats for two hundred and fifty. Even that is too many. The great mass of the theatre-goers don't go to *The Soul Call*; they are all round the corner in a huge picture house (capacity three thousand) looking at *Big-Hearted Jim, A Film of Western Life, Through which blows the Ozone of the Cow Pasture*. That's the stuff they want. But the really cultivated people want to know whether Helga should or should not have poisoned her husband, and whether Mabel should or should not live with Lionel Derwent. So they are all there in evening clothes, with other people's wives with white necks and plenty of jewels in their hair. Hence the setting of *The Soul Call* is not a bit like the setting of the old melodrama with the huge theatre full of noise and clatter, the boys shouting "Pea-nuts! Programme!"

In the Little Theatre all is quiet, with just dim red lights here and there, and noiseless ushers selling the Book of the Play on embossed paper for fifty cents. This is the only kind of atmosphere

in which people can properly analyse the Problem
of Marriage.

When the Piffle-Play begins, the curtain doesn't
go up ; it is parted in the middle and silently drawn
aside by a thing in black silk knee-breeches. When
it is drawn back, the scene is a room. It is called
" A Room in the Derwents' Residence," and it is
evidently just " a room." The stage of the old
melodrama had wings and flies and drops and open
spaces up above, and glimpses at the sides of actors
not wanted and waiting till they were. But the
stage of the Piffle-Play is made into a room, with a
real ceiling and real doors, and a real fire burning
in a real grate.

By the time the audience have examined this,
they see that there is an ineffective young man
in a grey tweed suit seated at a little table on the
left, playing solitaire with a pack of cards.

He flings down a card, and he exclaims, " Oh,
hang these cards ! " then calls, " Meadows ! I say,
Meadows ! " The audience, by looking up on
their programmes " the characters in the order of
their appearance," know that the ineffective young
man at the table is Lionel Derwent, husband of
Mabel Derwent. The Book of the Play explains
to them that " Lionel Derwent is the type of young
man who would rather smoke a cigarette than work
in a coal mine. In appearance he looks as if a

proposition in solid geometry would bore him. He is quite visibly a man who might be fond of a Pekingese dog, but one sees at once that he would not care to attend an Hotel Men's Annual Convention at Niagara-on-the-Lake." Reading this, the audience know exactly what sort of man he is.

When Derwent calls "Meadows! I say, Meadows!" in comes the butler. Derwent says, "Get me some more cards, will you, Meadows? These are perfectly rotten"; and Meadows says, "Yes, sir, at once, sir," exactly as a butler would say it. The acting is so perfect that it isn't acting at all. Meadows is, or at least *was*, a butler. That's how he got the part. In the old melodrama days the actor made the part. Now the part makes the actor. The old-time actor used to act anything and everything. One day he was a villain, the next a hero; one day old, the next young. One week he was 6 feet high, the next he had shrunk to 5 feet 4 inches. He acted a bishop one night and an idiot the next. It was all the same to him. Bring him anything and he'd act it.

But in the Piffle-Play on the New Stage the actor is cast for his part. When they want a man to act as a butler they don't advertise for actors; they advertise for butlers.

Meadows has in his hand a little silver tray with a card on it, and he says:

" Mr. Chown is downstairs, sir. May I show him up ? "

Derwent says, " Queen—four—Queen,—yes, do, Meadows."

Derwent goes on, " King—six—eight . . ." till the door opens again, and Meadows announces " Mr. Chown."

In comes another young man with a hat and stick in his hand. This is Charles Chown. He is just as well dressed as Derwent (only well-dressed people can get into a Piffle-Play), but he looks somewhat rougher in texture. In fact, the book says of him :

" Charles Chown is evidently the kind of man who would react more vigorously to a share of Canadian Pacific Railway stock than to a bunch of carnations. His air is that of a man who would fail to read a page of Bergson's philosophy but would like a marginal option in an oil company. He would probably prefer a Cattle Show to a meeting of Secondary School Teachers."

So we know exactly what Charles Chown is like.

Lionel says languidly, " Ah, Charles. Sit down— ace—ten—Queen———"

" I've just run in for a minute," says Chown, " to give you your cigarette case. You left it at our house last night. Still nothing better to do than play solitaire, eh ? "

" My dear fellow, what *is* there to do ? Everything's been done long ago."

Chown grunts.

" After all, what is there in *life* ? One simply *lives*."

Chown grunts.

" Take the thing any way you will, I'm hanged if I can see anything more in existence than simply existing. One breathes, but why ? "

Chown grunts. He evidently doesn't see why.

" I mean, here one is. Did one ask to be ? Hardly. It is a matter in which one had no say. One wasn't consulted."

At this point Lionel Derwent gets up and walks over to the mantelpiece, where he takes a cigarette and lights it. This thrilling piece of action quite palpably lifts the whole play up.

Charles Chown goes and puts his hat and stick down on a table, and pulls a chair near the fire and lights a cigar. This again is a regular thriller. In fact, the action of the play is getting too wild altogether. So Lionel and Charles go back to their analysis of life. Some of the audience, who don't understand that they are " analysing life," wonder what in Hades they're talking about. But these are uncultivated people who have no business in the Little Theatre, and ought to be at *Big-Hearted Jim*, next door. The bulk of the audience is fascinated.

Chown speaks : " That's all right, Derwent, but it's all rot (*puff*). You ought to come down to the Exchange (*puff*) some morning. Then you'd know that there's something doing in life (*puff*)."

" My dear fellow ! "

" *This* morning, for instance. Steel fell fifteen points."

Lionel, very languidly, " Fell down or fell up ? "

" Why, down, of course. You never heard such a racket as the fellows made."

" How can they care about it ? "

" Why, hang it, think of the *money* it meant ! "

" Money ! Oh, I say, Chown, money ! Come, come ! "

Lionel, who has been standing, stretches his elbows with a yawn and walks over and stands looking at a picture and muttering, " Money ! I say, Chown, that's rather thick !—money ! "

Lionel's acting when he yawns is simply admirable. In fact, it was principally his yawn that got him where he is. In the old melodrama a good actor was one who could handle a broadsword in a Highland duelling scene, or leap off a lighthouse into the sea. In the Piffle-Play it means one who can yawn.

" Well, I must skip along," says Chown. " I must get down to the Exchange. So long."

When Chown goes out, Lionel shrugs his shoulders as he lights another cigarette.

"What a clod!" he murmurs. Then he pushes a bell button and calls out, "Meadows!"

The butler reappears.

"Will you kindly dust off that chair where Mr. Chown was sitting."

"Yes, sir."

Lionel watches Meadows dusting the chair for a minute. Then he says:

"I say, Meadows."

"Yes, sir."

"Has it ever occurred to you, Meadows, that some men have souls about the size of a share of preferred stock?"

"No, sir, I can't say it has; ah, excuse me, sir, there's the bell."

In another half-minute Meadows reopens the door with the words:

"Mrs. Chown."

Helga Chown comes sliding into the room. She is dark, very beautiful, and as slender as a liqueur glass. Her clothes are pure Art, and droop on her like a butterfly's wings.

As to her character, the audience know all about it already from reading about *The Soul Call* before they see it; and anyway they have the Book of the Play, which says:

"Helga, the wife of Charles Chown, is a woman whose soul has overgrown her body. Life presses on her on all sides, and she cannot escape. She beats her wings against the bars in vain."

On the old-fashioned stage this " beating her wings against the bars " might have been misunderstood. But not so now.

Derwent rises, and they come together, saying, " Helga ! " and " Lionel ! " with an infinite depth of meaning.

Helga draws off her gloves and drops into a chair.

" Charles here ? " she says.

" Just left. Did you want to see him ? "

" No, to not see him. Give me a cigarette."

Lionel comes over near her and gives her a cigarette and lights it.

" Where's Mabel ? " she asks.

" Gone out to the Dog Show ! "

They both shudder.

" And Charles ? "

" Went down to the Stock Exchange."

They both shiver.

The audience are following the play with great expectancy and growing excitement. They don't expect a passionate love scene. They know better than that. But Lionel and Helga are going to " analyse themselves " ! and the audience are waiting for it.

Lionel starts first.

" How easy people like Charles and Mabel seem to find life ! "

Helga nods. " Yes, don't they."

" They never seem to stop to analyse themselves."

" Perhaps," murmurs Helga, " they can't."

This terrible thought holds them both silent for a minute. Then Helga speaks.

" Lionel," she says, " lately I've been trying to think it all out, what it all means. I want to see it all clearly—you and me and everything——"

Lionel has taken her hand very gently.

" Yes, dear ? " he murmurs.

" No, don't—I mean, don't take my hand, not now." She turns to him with a perplexed beautiful face. " I want to *think !* "

It is evidently so difficult for her to think that if he takes her hand he'll queer it.

" I want to think it all out, and when I think about it I want to be all *me*—can't you understand ? —just me and not a bit *you*. Do you know how I mean ? "

" I think I do, dear."

He doesn't really ; but this is the kind of lie that must be told.

Helga goes on with rising animation, breaking into passionate analysis of herself.

" Sometimes I sit by myself and think, and try

74

to analyse myself, and everything seems so small and myself so small too, as if nothing mattered, just like an infinitely small bit of something bigger, something lost in itself and looking for itself in itself. You know what I mean."

" I think I do."

" Often it seems as if there were just nothing."

" I know," Lionel murmurs.

" And then, sometimes, it seems as if there must be something."

" I know," murmurs Lionel again.

Then they are both silent. Presently Helga speaks in a more commonplace tone :

" Doesn't it seem queer, Lionel, how people just go on living ? Take Charles and Mabel. There they are, two commonplace, ordinary people. They go about together—to Dog Shows and things, and that seems to be enough—I suppose they like each other and that's all—they seem satisfied—and with you and me it's so different—people like them don't seem to know when the soul calls to another soul."

" I know," Lionel murmurs. His part in the play here is very difficult. He has to sit and look like a soul and keep murmuring " I know," and he can't even yawn.

Helga goes on :

" The other night at that silly Dog Show, as

soon as I saw you I could feel my soul calling to yours, right over the dogs, and at the Cat Show, the same thing. But Charles and Mabel don't seem to feel things like that. At the Dog Show they seemed to be looking at the Dogs. Just imagine ! "

There is a long silence, and then Lionel gets up and walks the whole length of the room and back again and sits down again. This dramatic piece of action means that something is coming.

He speaks.

" Helga," he says, " I only mention this as an idea. Have you ever thought of poison ? "

Helga very calmly takes out a cigarette from a case and lights it very deliberately. The audience are desperately anxious. Has she or has she not ?

" Have I ever thought of poison ? Poison for whom ? Do you mean for us, for you and me ? "

" Oh dear, no. For Charles and Mabel. Mind, it's only an idea. If you don't like it I'll say no more about it."

Helga turns to him a face of passionate yearning.

" Yes, Lionel, I have thought of it—often and often. In fact, I came over here to talk of it. Every time I look at Charles I feel that the only way my soul can grow is to poison him."

" I know," Lionel murmurs. " I feel that way

76

toward Mabel, and it's only just to her, poor girl, to poison her."

Presently Helga says, "When can we do it?"

"To-day would be all right. Mabel's going to tea with you this afternoon, isn't she? We can arrange it for then."

"But I don't know whether I have any poison in the house. I am so unpractical a housekeeper, you know, dear."

"That doesn't matter. I'll tell Meadows to get some and take it over to Annette, your maid."

"But then Meadows would know."

"So he would. But that needn't matter. One could poison Meadows too."

"But Annette?"

"The simplest thing would be to poison Annette as well. After all, what does life mean for people like Annette and Meadows? They breathe, but that's all."

"And after it's over?"

Lionel and Helga have risen, and he draws close to her and puts his hand on her shoulder and is looking into her eyes.

"After it's over then we shall be *free*, free to be ourselves and go away, far, far away—together——"

They embrace, and when they break away Lionel leads Helga to the door and shows her out.

Then he goes and sits down again and picks up

a newspaper to read. After a minute he rings the bell. Meadows comes.

" I say, Meadows. Pack up a trunk of my things. I'm going away to-night."

" Yes, sir."

" And, Meadows, I wish you'd be good enough to go out and get a packet of arsenic."

" Yes, sir."

" Get enough to—let me see——"

" To poison an animal, sir ? "

" Yes, four animals. Thank you, Meadows."

And with that the two sides of the curtain fall slowly together and the act is over.

In the old melodrama when the curtain fell there was always a wild burst of music, and bright lights, and shouts of " Pea-nuts ! " Not so in this. Only very soft lights, mostly red, are turned on, and mere wisps of music thin as smoke.

Meantime everybody discusses the play. In the old days the men used to go out and drink. Now they stay in and discuss. There is a general feeling among the women that Helga is quite right in proposing to poison Charles. Till she does that, she can never expand. The case of Mabel being poisoned is not clear. The audience haven't seen her yet, so they can't tell. But it is certain that two commonplace people like Charles and Mabel have no right to prevent Lionel and Helga following the higher call of their natures. The discussion is still at its height when the curtain slides aside on

ACT II

The Drawing-room of the Chown Residence

And there are Lionel Derwent and his wife Mabel, being shown in by Annette, the stage maid.

It is a large and sumptuous room, with a real ceiling like the one in the first act, and with real mahogany furniture and Chippendale chairs and vases of Beauty roses—in fact, just like the rooms that the audience have come out of. There are tea-things on a large Hindoo brass tray on eight legs.

Mabel Derwent goes over to the Hindoo tray and picks up a big cream-candy out of a box and eats it, and says, "Yum! Yum!" with animal relish. All the audience look at Mabel. They see in her a dashing, good-looking woman, a blonde, all style, and with just a touch of loudness. All the women in the audience decide at once that she ought to be poisoned; but the men aren't so sure.

Mabel says, "I say, Lionel, do eat one of these. They're just scrumptious."

This is meant to show how terribly material she is.

Lionel just shrugs his shoulders in mute appeal to heaven.

Mabel walks around the room looking at things. She picks up a book and reads the title, " *Bergsonian Illusionism.*" She says, " Oh, help ! " and drops it.

This shows how uncultivated she is.

Presently she says, " Wonder where Charles is. If he's out in the stables I'll go out and dig him up. He told me he has a new hunter, a regular corker. Suppose we go out to the stables."

Lionel says with great languor, " Thank you. I take no interest in stables."

By this time the audience are supposed to have the exact measure of Mabel Derwent—materialism, ignorance, candy, and the horse stable. But even at that, a lot of the men would refuse to poison her. Her figure is too good. On the other hand, all the thin women in the audience think her too fat. The amount of fat permitted to actresses in the Piffle-Play is a matter of great nicety. They have to be cast for it as carefully as tallow candles.

So, as the audience now know exactly what Mabel Derwent is like, the play passes on.

Charles Chown comes briskly in, shaking hands with both of them. " Hullo, Mabel. How do you do, Lionel; so sorry to keep you waiting. I think Helga's in the conservatory. She'll be here in a minute."

At which Lionel Derwent says, " In the conservatory ? Then I think I'll go and look for her.

I want to see that new begonia that Helga's so keen about."

And with that out he goes, leaving Charles and Mabel together, as they are meant to be.

And just the minute they are alone, Mabel comes close up to Charles and looks all round and says, " Well ? " in quite a different voice from anything she has used before. So the audience are certain that there is going to be something doing.

Charles says, " It's all right. Everything all arranged."

And Mabel says, " Good boy," and then she says, " Take that," and comes and gives him a kiss— a real one, one with no new art or new thought about it.

Charles goes on. " It's all arranged. We'll go out to the stables presently, and I've got a taxi coming round there with your things in it."

" And it's all right about the trains ? "

" Right as rain," says Charles, drawing out a railroad folder. " We get the 5.30 at the Central, change trains half an hour out of town to get the Havana boat to-morrow evening."

" Lovely ! " Mabel says, and then repeats, more slowly and thoughtfully, " Lovely ! and yet do you know, Charlie, now that it's come at last, I feel— don't you know ?—half afraid—or not that—but don't you know ? "—hesitating.

Charles says, "Nonsense!" and is just about to draw her to him when the door opens and Lionel and Helga come in. Lionel says to his wife :

"Helga's just been showing me her new begonia —a most amazing thing."

And Mabel says, "A new begonia. Where did it come from, Helga ? "

And Helga answers, "From Havana. They grow so beautifully there. I should just love to see Havana. Shouldn't you ? "

This little touch makes quite a hit with the audience. The irony of truth always does. As a matter of fact, Sophocles started it four or five hundred years before Christ. But they don't know it. They think it awfully up-to-date.

After this there's a little random conversation just to fill up time, and then Charles says :

"I say, Mabel, how would you like to come out to the stables and see my new mare before we have tea ? "

And Mabel answers :

"Oh, I'd love to ! I wanted to ask you about her. Come along. We won't be long, Helga."

And with that they go out, and Lionel and Helga are left together.

Just as soon as they are alone Helga says :

"So you're off the poison idea ? "

" Clear off it," says Lionel; " as I told you just now, I don't think it's worth it."

" Worth it ? "

" Yes, I mean it would involve such a terrible fuss and nuisance. Here's the poison—Meadows got it all right."

Lionel takes from his pocket a large packet in light green paper, marked with a skull and cross-bones, and labelled ARSENIC in large letters.

" We can use it, if you like. I'm not awfully particular. Only I don't believe that much would kill Mabel anyway."

Helga takes the packet of poison and holds it in her hand, musing.

" But think," she murmurs, " of the relief of death. Think of the relief to a person of Charles's temperament to be dead——"

" Oh, I know that. And, for that matter, Meadows ought to be glad to be dead. But you see, Helga, it isn't done."

Lionel walks across the stage and lights a cigarette.

" But what can we do ? " says Helga. She clasps her hands about her knees as she sits. When she does that the audience know at once that she is going to analyse herself. " Do you ever look into yourself, Lionel, deep, deep into yourself ? I do. Sometimes I try to picture to myself that it's not me but just something inside of me. Do you know what I mean, dear ? "

" I think I do," murmurs Lionel.

They're off. For the next ten minutes Helga plunges into a fierce analysis of herself. As the critics of the play say afterwards, she " bares her soul," and when she has bared it it's " the soul of a woman buffeted by the intense light of self-perplexity and finding no anchorage in it."

When she is finished, or as nearly finished as she is likely to be, Lionel says, " Then I suppose we must simply go on as we are."

" I suppose so, Lionel. If, as you say, Charles and Mabel have a right to live, it seems as if we have to be satisfied."

" Perhaps it does," says Lionel. He takes a turn up and down the room and then he says : " There's just one thing I've thought about, Helga. It's only an idea, so of course you can say no to it at once, if there's nothing in it. But couldn't we perhaps just get on a train together and go away together ? "

" Where ? " says Helga.

" Oh, just anywhere. It's only an idea. You mentioned Havana just now. Couldn't we just get a train or a boat or something and go to Havana ? "

" I don't know, Lionel. It all seems so strange. I must *think*."

Helga presses her hand to her forehead : this is always a sign that she is thinking, or trying to. Lionel lets her think undisturbed.

" I don't know, Lionel; I must think it all out. I must analyse myself and try to analyse Havana. Listen, Lionel, let me think a month. Perhaps it will be clearer then. . . ."

Lionel looks at his watch.

" I say," he says, " Charles and Mabel seem a long time in looking at that mare. How strange it seems that commonplace people like Charles and Mabel can know nothing of the kind of thing that means so much to us. I suppose they never stop to think."

" They never analyse themselves," murmurs Helga.

And just then there is a light knock at the door, and Annette steps in with an envelope on a tray.

" Mr. Chown asked me to give you this letter, ma'am, after he had gone."

" Gone ? "

" Yes, ma'am, he went away in a taxi with Mrs. Derwent."

" In a taxi ? "

" Yes, ma'am, with luggage in it."

" A taxi with luggage ?   Give me the letter."

Annette presents the letter and goes out.

85

Helga takes the letter, tears open the envelope, and reads aloud :

" Dear Helga,
    "Mabel and I have decided to go away together. We are taking a train South this afternoon. I have made every arrangement for you in regard to money and that sort of thing, and of course now you will be completely free. We shall not be in your way at all, as we are going far away—in fact, we are going to Havana ! "

As Helga finishes reading, she and Lionel remain looking at each other.

" To Havana ! " they both repeat, and then there is a little silence.

After which Lionel says, " Do you know, Helga, it rather occurs to me that it's the commonplace people who *do* things."

On which the curtain comes sliding together, and the audience rises and wraps its furs round its neck, and goes home with a Piffle-Problem theme to ponder over, and with an impression of profound thought.

IV—"*Oroastus*," a *Greek Tragedy*

(*As presented in our Colleges*)

THE Greek Drama, as everybody knows, possesses a majesty that we do not find elsewhere. It has a loftiness, a sublimity, to which no later theatre has attained. Anybody who has seen the play of *Alcestis* put on by the senior class of the Podunk High School will admit this at once.

The Greek Drama, unfortunately, is no longer exhibited to the ordinary theatre-going public.

It is too sublime for them. They are away beneath it. The attempt to put on one act of the *Œdipus Polyphlogistus* of Boanerges at the entertainment evening of the annual convention of the rubber men of America last January was voted down by a nine-to-one vote in favour of having Highland dances of the Six Susquehanna Sisters.

Another difficulty is that a lot of the Greek Drama is lost. Some critics think that all the best of it is lost; others say, not all; others again claim that what we have ought to make us feel

87

that we have no right to complain over what is lost.

But though the Greek Drama is not presented in our commercial theatres, it still flourishes in our institutions of learning. One may yet see the stupendous tragedies of Sophocles and Euripides put on in the auditorium of the Jefferson High School, or acted, under pressure, by the boys of St. Peter's (Episcopal) Resident Academy, or presented in commencement week by the Fi Fi Omega (Oil) Fraternity of the University of Atalanta.

The open season for the Greek Drama in the college is the month of February. This gives the students four months to learn the Greek lines, and is based on a piece-work rate of five words a day. After the play they have still time to get back to what is now called " normaley " before the end of the college session.

Let us therefore transport ourselves in fancy to the winter evening in a college town when the Greek play is to be put on by the senior class in Classics. There is no unusual light or brilliance in the streets to announce this fact. On the contrary, the general appearance is as of gloom. Here and there a glaring light against a boarding brazenly announces the vulgar fact that Harold Lloyd, or rather the shade of him, is revolving at the Coliseum. But of the fact that the shade of Sophocles is to

be at the auditorium of the Faculty of Liberal
Arts there is no public indication. Nor is the
location of Sophocles easy to find. Our first attempt to follow what seems to be the movement
of the crowd leads us vainly towards the entrance
of Third Street Skating Rink, and then to the
lighted portico of the Gaiety Burlesque Theatre,
Ladies Cordially Welcomed. No such lighted
path leads to the august dead. Nor are the services
of a taxi of any use to us. The driver has not heard
of the performance, is not aware apparently of the
existence of the college auditorium, and can only
suggest that Sophocles himself may be staying at
the *Jefferson*. Most of the actors do.

But to anybody accustomed to colleges and their
ways it is not difficult to find the auditorium. One
has but to notice here and there among the elm-
trees of the side streets a few shivering figures
moving in the same direction and wearing a costume
half-way between fashion and disreputability. These
are college professors, and they are going to the
play. Let us follow them.

We do this, and we easily find the auditorium—
in fact, on a close inspection we can distinctly see
light here and there in its windows, and people
going in. Entrance is effected in two ways : either
by ticket, for those who have tickets, or without a
ticket, for those who haven't got a ticket. When

we are well inside the place, we find a large placard, visible only to those who have got in, announcing the attraction :

A GREAT TRAGEDY

THE GREEK PLAY

OROASTUS

PUT ON IN THE ORIGINAL
BY THE SENIOR CLASS

A MASTERPIECE OF SORROW
DON'T MISS IT
"ALL UP"

There is quite a sprinkling of people already seated. There must be what is called "easily three hundred." But on such occasions nobody is mean enough to count the audience. We are shown to our seats by girl ushers in college gowns and bobbed hair, a touch of old Greek life which goes to our heart.

If the senior class understood advertising as well

as they know Greek, they would have put that placard near the railway station and had a band playing, and one or two of the girls with bobbed hair selling tickets behind glass. Nor would it have been necessary to select the girls who know most Greek. But still—we started by saying that the Greek Drama was lofty : let it remain so.

When we get to our seats we realize that we needn't have come for a long time yet. There is no evidence of anybody starting anything, Greek or otherwise. There is a subdued chatter among the audience, and people straggling in, one, two, and even three at a time. We notice presently that all the audience in the hall except ourselves have got little books or pamphlets—paper things that look like the uplift hymns at a Rotary Club six o'clock supper, or the hymnal of a Chautauqua Society. We go back to the outer entrance and get one (fifty cents each), and find that this priceless thing is the book of the play with the Greek on one side and the English (it seems English) on the other. So now we can take our seats again and study the thing out.

On the outside of the book of the play is an announcement for

KOLLEGE KLOTHES

Superb Suits, $13.50. *Classy Overcoats,* $9.50

—but we had always known that education was a struggle, and we pass this by.

On the inside the thing begins in earnest.

It is still a little sprinkled with advertisements here and there, but we rightly gathered that they are not essential to the tragedy. The book runs thus :

OROASTUS

KOLLEGE KLOTHES AND STUDENTS BOOTS. A Greek Drama dating probably from the fifth century STUDENTS SHIRTS before Christ. The play is generally attributed to Diplodocus, who lived probably at Megara but also perhaps KNIT TO FIT UNDERWEAR FOR COLLEGE MEN at Syracuse. His work ALL WOOL is generally esteemed on a par with that of his great contemporaries IAMBILICHUS AND EUARBILIUS. He is said on what seems credible ground to have died during the presentation of one of his own plays. But the place of his death THIRD AVENUE AND JEFFERSON STREET. THE HOME LUNCH RESORT is unknown.

The entire works of Diplodocus with the single extant exception of *Oroastus* are lost, but they are none the less esteemed

on that account. A full account of his life
was written by Polybius, but is lost.
(RAH! RAH! JOIN THE MANDOLIN CLUB.)
A critique of his genius written by Dio-
genes Laertius, but attributed also to Pliny,
has perished. The bust of Diplodocus,
said to be the work of Phidias Senior, was
lost, either at sea or on land. The bust
now in the Louvre was executed one
thousand six hundred years after his supposed death, and may or may not show
him as he was. Internal evidence goes to
show that Diplodocus was, internally, very
unhappy TRY POSSUM'S PILLS ONE A DAY.
From the play before us many lines have
unfortunately been lost. But the loss is
in every case indicated by asterisks in the
text GET YOUR NECKTIES AT APPLETON'S.

The simple theme of sorrow, the rigour
of fate, and the emptiness of human
desire dominate the play HAVE YOU JOINED
THE BIBLE CLASS? NOW IS THE TIME
TO JOIN.

And at this point the solid Greek begins, pages
and pages of it, and facing it on the other side
solid masses of English. And just as we begin to
try and study it out—we ought really to have

begun a month ago—we realize that the entertainment is beginning.

. . . . .

The huge white sheet that acts as a curtain slides sideways, groaning on a wire, and behold the platform of the auditorium, converted into the severe stage of the Greeks, with white curtains on the sides and a bare floor, and of stage properties no trace. No comfortable little red mica fire burning at the side such as cheers the actors of a drawing-room play; none of the green grass and the cardboard inn with the swinging sign that stand for eighteenth-century comedy; nothing of the sweep of rock and the curtain of cloud that indicates that Forbes Robertson is about to be Hamlet. Nothing, just nothing; boards, a little sawdust, room to come in and out, and sorrow. That is all that the Greeks asked or wanted. How infinitely superior to ourselves, who have so piled up panoply of life about us that our lightest acts and our deepest grief must alike be hung with priceless decorations. But the Greek Theatre, like the four bare walls of the Puritan House of Worship——but stop, the play has started.

A tall figure walks in, a player in a long draped sheet of white, a bearded player, with a chaplet of leaves about his head. . . . This must be Oroastus—let me look; yes, it's Oroastus, King of Thebes.

What's he saying ? A sort of long-drawn howling, " Aie ! Aie ! Aie ! Aie ! " My ! My ! Oroastus must be in a terrible way.

Aie ! Aie ! Aie ! Aie !

This must be that note of sorrow that I spoke about ; or else it is some of the internal melancholy of Diplodocus.

Oroastus, King of Thebes, walks out pretty well into the middle of the stage and stands there groaning, " Aie ! Aie ! Aie ! . . ."

So to get a clue to what is now going to happen, we look at our book of the play to see that the next thing marked in the English text is :

Entry of the Chorus.

Ah now ! Cheer up ! That's something like. The Chorus ! Bring them right along in. No doubt they will be of that beautiful type of classic Greek girls. If there is one thing that we specialize on in the modern drama, it is the Chorus. Fetch the girls in by all means.

In they come. Help ! What is this ? Three old men—very aged, with cotton-wool beards and long white robes like the one Oroastus wears.

No, there is no doubt about it, the Greek idea of a Chorus is a matter on which we take issue at once. These three old men may think themselves terribly cute, but for us, quite frankly, they are not in it. We knew before we came that the Greek Tragedy was severe, but this is a pitch of severity for which we were not prepared.

However, as these three saucy old men are on the stage, let's see what they're doing. Look, they all lift their arms up straight above their heads, and they all begin to moan :

Aie ! Aie ! Aie—e !

In fact, just like King Oroastus. They evidently have got the same internal trouble that he has.

Now they seem to be breaking into a kind of sustained talk in a sort of chant. It's impossible to know what they are saying, because it's all in Greek—or, no—of course we can follow it. We have the English in the book of the play ; in fact, you can see all the people in the audience turning the leaves of their little book and burying their heads in them up to their spectacles. At a Greek college play the audience don't look at the stage; they look at the little book.

This is what the three saucy old men are saying :

O how unhappy is this (now standing before us) King !

O Fate ! with what dark clouds art thou about to overwhelm (or perhaps to soak) him.

96

O what grief is his ! and how on the one
hand shall he for his part escape it. O
woe ! O anxiety, O grief, O woe !

In other words, in the Greek play the business
of the Chorus is to come in and tell the audience
what a classy spectacle it is going to be. Sorrow
being the chief idea of Greek Tragedy, the Chorus
have to inform the audience what they're going
to get, and to get it good. It's a great idea in
dramatic construction. It's just as if at the beginning of *Hamlet* the Chorus stuck their heads over
the battlements of Elsinore and said, in up-to-date
English, " Say, look at this young man ! Isn't
he going to get it in the neck ? Eh, what ? Isn't
he in for hard luck ? Just wait till his father's
ghost gets a twist on him."

So the Chorus groan and the King keeps howling,
" Aie, aie, aie ! " and after they've done it long
enough, the three Chorus walk out, one behind the
other, like the figures on an Athenian frieze, and
the King is left alone.

He speaks (and a footnote in the book says that
this speech is one of the finest things in Greek
Tragedy) :

What awful fate hangs over (or perhaps
overhangs) me, this unhappy King!
What sorrow now does the swift-moving

97

hand (or perhaps the revolving finger) of Doom make for me!

Where shall I turn? Whither shall I go? What is going to hit me next?

What would I not give, even if it were my palace itself, to be let loose from this overwhelming anxiety (or perhaps this rather unusual situation)?

Beside it, my palace and my crown are nothing.

The King pauses, and lifts his two hands straight up in the air, and cries:

O Zeus, what next?

And at this juncture the little book says:

Enter a Herald.

And the audience look up from their books a minute to see this Herald come in. In runs the Herald. He is young and has no beard. He has a tunic and bare legs, and on his feet are sandals with wings, and on his head also are wings, and he carries a wand. The wings on his feet are meant to show how fast he could go if he really had to—like the bicycle that the telegraph messenger pushes along with him. The wand means that if he needed to he could fly.

The entrance of this Herald causes the only

interruption from the audience that occurs during the play. There are cries from the gallery of " Attaboy ! Good work, Teddy ! " The Herald is one of the most popular members of the Fi Fi Omega Society. Anybody looking at that Herald approves of him. He is the best stage effect of the lot. In fact, there is more " pep " about the Herald than in all the rest put together.

He confronts Oroastus and they hold a dialogue like this :

> O King.
> O Herald.
> Aie !
> Me, too.
> Woe, woe ! King.
> I believe you.
> Things are bad.
> They are indeed. What misfortune brings you in this direction ?
> A grave one.
> I guess it must be ; but tell me that my ear may hear it.
> Grievous are my tidings.
> I am sure they are.
> And hard for you to hear.

. . . . .

The slowness of the Herald in giving the bad

news to the King is one of the striking things in the Greek Drama. It is only equalled on the modern stage by the great detective revealing the mystery in the fifth act, or a lawyer explaining the terms of the secret will, or the dying criminal (shot, deservedly, in a cellar) confessing the innocence of the heroine. In fact, the Greek Herald was the man who started this kind of trouble. He was the first original exponent of the idea of not telling a good thing in a hurry.

He speaks again :

Things are not what they seem.

Oroastus groans "Oh!" All the dialogue has by this time been knocked out of him. The Herald realizes that he can't get another rise out of him. So he gets down to facts :

Your palace, O King, has on the one hand been destroyed by fire and your crown, which in and of itself for the most part signified your kingship, has on the other hand been stolen.

OROASTUS : Aie, aie, aie ! My palace is destroyed and my crown is lost. O whoa, this is grief.

THE HERALD : It is. Good-bye. I have other tasks (or perhaps avocations).

The Herald says this and withdraws; and as he goes out in come the three old Chorus men again. That was the great thing about the Greek Tragedy. It never stopped. It went right on. In the modern play when the Herald said " Good-bye," the curtain would fall on Act I. In the moving picture the scene would shift and show the palace being burnt. But the good old Greek Tragedy went right on, like sawing wood. This is called the unity of the drama, and so far nothing beats it.

The Chorus, of course, have merely come in to have a good time by piling up the sorrow and gloating over Oroastus.

They line up and they chant out :

> Oh ! look at this—now standing before us—King (or sometimes rendered this ordinary man). Sorrow has struck him.
> His palace and his crown are destroyed.
> But Fate is not done with him yet.
> All-compelling Fate is getting ready another arrow (or, perhaps, is going to take another crack at him).
> He has lost his palace.
> But watch out.
> There is more coming.

And at this the three miserable old brutes troop out again. Then the King says :

O me, alas ! My palace is gone and yet a further fate overhangs me. What is this hang-over ?

For so much, indeed, have I borne that to me now it seems that nothing further could overwhelm me, even if it were the loss of my tender consort herself.

And just as he says this, the sign goes up again in the book :

The Herald enters.

The King speaks :

What now ? And why have your feet brought you back ?

It was evident that a favourite theory of the Greek tragedians was that a man went where his feet took him. This was part of the general *necessity*, or rigour, of fate.

The Herald says :

Terrible are the tidings.
What are they ?
Something awful.
Tell me what they are.
How can I ?
Go at it (or perhaps go to it).
Dark indeed is the news and terrible is the certainty.

What is it ?

How can I say it ? It is dark.

What is the dark stuff that you are giving to me ? Does it perhaps concern my consort, the fair-fingered Apologee ?

It does.

How much ?

Very much.

Tell me then the whole extent of the matter, concealing nothing.

I will.

Do.

With my lips I will say it.

Do so.

The King groans. The Herald knows that the time has come to let loose his information. He says :

Listen, then, O King. Your queenly consort, the fair-fingered Apologee, has gone to Hades.

THE KING : Too bad !

THE HERALD : Gloomy Pluto has carried her off.

THE KING : This is deplorable (or perhaps reprehensible) !

THE HERALD : Good-bye. I have other avocations.

The Herald retires, and the King has hardly had

time to say " Aie ! " before the Chorus come trailing on again and take up their station. They cant out :

> Look at this.
> How's this for grief ?

The royal consort has been carried off by the Gloomy Dis, he of the long ears, to his dark home. But sorrow is not yet done. There is a whole lot more coming. " For such is the fate of Kings. Either they have a good time or they don't." With this sentiment the Chorus all troop off again. We gather from the little book, even if we didn't know it already, that their last sentiment, "Either they have a good time or they don't," is considered one of the gems of the Greek Drama. The commentators say that this shows us the profundity of the mind of Diplodocus. Some think that this places him above the lighter work of such men as Iambilichus or Euarbilius. Others again claim that this passage, " Either they have a good time or they don't," shows (internally, of course) that the life of Diplodocus was not all sorrow. To write this, Diplodocus must himself have had a good time some of the time. In fact, these lines, we are given to understand, have occasioned one of those controversies which have made the Greek Drama what it is.

King Oroastus, being now left alone, starts a new

fit of sorrow: " Aie, aie, aie! "—in fact, just as we
expected he would. By this time we have grasped
the idea of the tragedy: the successive blows of
sorrow that hit Oroastus one after the other.
First the Chorus say, " There'll be sorrow," then
Oroastus says, " Here comes a sorrow," and then
the Herald comes in and says, " Get ready now,
stand by for a new sorrow," and lands it at him.
There's a beautiful simplicity about it that you
never see on the stage to-day. In fact, this is
that sublimity, that loftiness, that only the Fi Fi
Omega players can catch.

So the King groans:

> Oh, what an absolutely complete sorrow
> this is, this last one!
> O Apologee!
> O Hades!
> For me, what now is left? My palace is
> destroyed, and the fair-fingered Apologee
> has gone to Hades. What now is left to
> me but my old dog?
> Old dog that I am myself on the one
> hand, my old dog on the other hand is all.

This passage, " Old dog that I am myself," is
indicated in the text as one of the high spots.
In fact, it is a joke. The text says so. From where
we sit we can see the Professor of Greek laughing

at it. Indeed, we could easily prove by looking up the large editions of the play that this is a joke. The commentators say : "The bitter jest of Oroastus in calling himself an 'old dog' illustrates for us the delicious irony of the great tragedian. Certain commentators have claimed indeed that the passage is corrupt, and that Oroastus called himself not an 'old dog' but a 'hot dog.' We prefer, however, the earlier reading, which seems to us exquisite. Diplodocus undoubtedly felt that the weight of sorrow at this point had become more than Oroastus or even the spectators could bear. By calling himself an 'old dog' he removes exactly that much of it."

This contention seems pretty well sustained. In fact, anybody accustomed to the modern stage will realize that we are here at the source of the alleviating joke, introduced at any moment of terrible tension. In the modern play a comic character is carried all through the piece in order to make these jokes. But the Greek Tragedy was nothing if not simple, direct, and honest. The hero has to make his own jokes.

Still, we are keeping the Herald waiting. The time is ripe for him to come in again.

Enter the Herald.

In he comes just as before (the Greeks didn't

believe in vanity), and the King at once asks him
the usual question about his feet :

> For what purpose, O Herald (he in-
> quires), do your feet bring you this way
> again ?
> THE HERALD : A gloomy one.
> Let me have it.
> I will.
> Do. For, however dark it is, I being now
> an old dog (or perhaps a hot dog), have no
> further consolation in life than my dog.

It is to be noticed that Diplodocus here uses
the same joke twice. Anybody who deals in
humour will warmly approve of this. To get the
best out of a joke it must be used over and over
again. In this matter the Greeks have nothing
on us.

This time the Herald knows that Oroastus can't
stand for much more. So he says :

> Old dog, indeed ? Did your lips lead you
> to say " old dog " ?
> They did indeed.
> Are you perhaps under the impression,
> O King, that you still have an old dog ?
> Such is my impression.
> In that case you never made a bigger
> mistake in your life.

Let me know it, and if indeed I have
made a mistake, let me hear it.

Hear it then. Your old dog is gone to
Hades. Good-bye. I have other avocations.

The Herald leaves, and the King breaks out into
lamentations :

Aie, aie (he says) ! My consort, the fair-
fingered Apologee, and my old dog are
in Hades. Why am I still left in the
upper air (or perhaps up in the air) ?
Oh whoa !

The King lifts his hands up in sorrow, and a
note in the book says : " King Oroastus has now
had nearly enough." To this we quite agree.
One might say, in fact, he had had plenty.

But the Chorus are not done with him yet.
On they come, with the remorselessness of the
Greek Drama.

They line up.

Look then at this (standing before us)
King. What a load he has !

But worse is yet coming. Keep your seats and
watch him.

They go out in their usual undisturbed way, and
Oroastus says :

Oh what a last final instalment (or hang-over) of bitter grief is now mine! What now is left ? Now that everything has gone to Hades, of what use is life itself ? Oh, day! Oh, sunshine! Oh, light! Let me withdraw myself, I, before my time, to my tomb, to my mausoleum which I have had made by the skilled hands of artificers, and there let me join hands with Death.

Oroastus has hardly said this when the Herald comes back. By this time everybody guesses the news that he brings. Under the circumstances not even a Greek Herald could string it out. The thing is too obvious.

The King says—well, there is no need to write it again—the Herald's feet, that same stuff ; but what he really means is, " Are you back again ? " And the Herald says, " Yes." This is the first plain answer that the Herald has given all through the play.

Then Oroastus says :

Is it dark stuff again ?

And the Herald says :

The darkest.

At which the King gives a groan and says :

Then let me not hear it, for already to me, thinking over pretty well everything, the matter seems more or less what you would call played out (or possibly worked to death). It is now in my mind, hearing nothing further, to retire to the mausoleum which I have long since caused to be built by skilled artificers, and there, lying down upon the stone, to clasp the hand of Death.

THE HERALD : You can't.

THE KING : Why not ? What is which ? For your words convey nothing. Tell me what it is.

THE HERALD : I will.

THE KING : Do.

THE HERALD : All right. Get ready for something pretty tough. Are you all set ? I am.

Know then, that your mausoleum no longer is. It was broken into by burglars and is unfit to use. Good-bye. I have other avocations.

OROASTUS : Aie, aie, aie ! . . .

Then they line up for a last crack at Oroastus :

Look at him !

Isn't he the unlucky bean (or perhaps turnip).

Did you ever hear of worse luck than his ?

Can you beat it ?

But such is life, Oroastus, and it is a necessity of the gods that even death is withheld from the sorrowful—" Aie, aie, aie ! "

And with that the play gives every symptom of being over. The white sheet that acts as the curtain glides down, and there is quite a burst of applause in the audience. The actors line up on the stage, and all the Fi Fi Omega crowd in the gallery call out, " Attaboy, Oroastus ! Good work, Teddy ! "

After which the audience doesn't break up as an ordinary theatre audience does, but coagulates itself into little knots and groups. It knows that presently coffee and sandwiches are going to be passed around, and the Greek Professor will stand in the middle of an admiring group while he explains to them that Oroastus is under the compulsion of ANANGKE.

But for us no cake nor coffee. Let us get back to the Jefferson Hotel grill-room while the supper is still on, and while we can still get places for the midnight vaudeville show, with the dances of the

Susquehanna Sextette and the black-faced comedian with the saxophone. This Greek stuff is sublime, we admit it; and it is lofty, we know it; and it has a dignity that the Susquehanna Sextette has not.

But, after seeing Greek Tragedy once, we know our level. And henceforth we mean to stick to it.

V—"*The Sub-Contractor*," *an Ibsen Play*

(*Done out of the Original Swedish with an Axe*)

DRAMATIS PERSONÆ

SLUMP	.	.	. *A Builder.*
VAMP	.	.	. *His Wife.*
DUMP	.	.	. *A Professor of Thermodynamics.*
SIMP .	.	.	. *A Maidservant.*
YOOP	.	.	. *An Accountant.*
SCOOP	.	.	. *His Sister.*
PASTOR GYMP	.		. *A Pastor.*
CRAMP	.	.	. *His Mother-in-law.*

Etc. etc. etc.

. . . and as many more with names of that kind and with occupations of that sort as there is room for on the page. Some of them may not get into the play at all. But that doesn't matter. An Ibsen *Dramatis Personæ* is a thing by itself.

SCENE.—A ROOM IN SLUMP'S HOUSE

(*There are flowers on the table*)

SLUMP : What beautiful flowers !
VAMP : Yes, they are fresh this morning.

> (SLUMP *and* VAMP *speak one after the
> other in short turns, like sawing*

113

*wood with a cross-cut saw. But
there is no need to indicate which
is speaking. It doesn't matter.*)

Are they indeed ?

Yes, they are.

How sweet they smell !

Yes, don't they ?

I like flowers.

So do I. I think they smell so beautiful.

It's a beautiful morning.

Yes, the spring will soon be here.

The air is deliciously fresh.

Yes it is, isn't it ?

I saw a bobolink in the garden.

A bobolink already ! Then the summer
is soon here.

Soon ; indeed, the meadows are already
green.

I like the green meadows.

Yes, isn't it ?

The angle of the sun is getting high.

I suppose it is. I noticed yesterday that
the diameter of the moon was less.

Much less, and the planets are brighter
than they were. Their orbits are
elongating.

I suppose so.

How I love the spring !

So do I. The evaporation of the air closes the pores of my skin.

.   .   .   .   .

This completes Round Number One. It is meant to show Swedish home-life, the high standard of education among the Swedes, and, just at the end, the passionate nature of Vamp. The spring fills her with longings. It also shows where Slump stands. For him the spring merely opens the pores of his skin.

With this understanding we are ready for a little action :

> (*A bell rings. Then* SIMP, *the maid, enters, showing in* DUMP, *a Professor of Thermodynamics.*)

Good morning, Dump. Good morning, Slump. Good morning, Vamp. Good morning, Dump.

DUMP : The spring will soon be here.

VAMP : I saw a bobolink in the garden.

DUMP : Yes, I saw a wagtail on the thatch of the dovecot.

SLUMP : Spring is coming.

DUMP : It will do my cough good. (*He coughs.*)

VAMP : Yes, you will soon be well.

DUMP : Never well. (*He coughs again.*)

SLUMP : You think too much. You need pleasure ; for me each time I finish a sub-contract I like to take my ease and drink sprott.

DUMP : I can't drink sprott. (*He coughs.*) I have
   a mortal disease.
VAMP : Don't say that.
DUMP : In six years I shall be dead.
      Nonsense. Come, drink a glass of sprott.
      No.
      Have some yip ?
      No.
      Take some pep ?
      No.
      (DUMP *goes and sits down near a window ;*
      the others look at him in silence.)

This completes Round Two. It is intended to
establish the fact that Dump has a mortal disease.
There is nothing visibly wrong with Dump except
that he looks bilious. But in every Ibsen play it
is understood that one of the characters has to
have a mortal disease. Dump in the Ibsen Drama
will die of biliousness in six years. Biliousness and
ill-temper take the place of *Anangke* in Greek
Tragedy.

      .   .   .   .   .

SLUMP : Well, I must be about my work. Come,
   Simp, and help me get my wallet and my
   compasses.
SIMP : Yes, sir. (SIMP *and* SLUMP *go out.* VAMP
   and DUMP *are left alone.*)

VAMP : Come and sit down.

DUMP : I don't want to sit down. I'm too ill to sit down.

VAMP : Here, get into this long chair ; let me make you comfortable.

(VAMP *makes* DUMP *sit down.*)

VAMP : There now, you're comfortable.

DUMP : Why should I be comfortable ? I'm too ill to be comfortable. In six years I shall be dead.

VAMP : Oh, no ! Don't say that.

DUMP : Yes, I will. The bile is mounting to my œsophagus.

VAMP : Oh, no !

DUMP : I say it is. There's an infiltration into my ducts. My bones are turning into calcareous feldspar.

This dialogue is supposed to bring out the full charm of Dump. The more bilious he is, the better Vamp likes him. It is a law of the Swedish drama that the heroines go simply crazy over bilious disagreeable men with only from six to twenty years to live. This represents the *everlasting mother-soul*. They go on talking :

VAMP : Let me sing to you.

DUMP : Yes, yes.

VAMP : Let me dance for you.
DUMP : Yes, yes ; dance for me.

Vamp is evidently smitten with that peculiar access of gaiety that is liable to overcome the heroine of an Ibsen play at any time. She dances about the room, singing as she goes :

> " Was ik en Butterflog
> Flog ik dein Broost enswog,
> Adjö, mein Hertzenhog,
> Adjë, Adjö ! "

DUMP (*passionately*) : More, more ; keep on singing. Keep on dancing. It exhilarates my capillary tissue. More, more.
VAMP : Do you love me ?
DUMP : I do.
VAMP : No, you mustn't say that. It's wicked to say that. What put that into your head ?
DUMP : Dance for me again.
VAMP : No. I mustn't. Listen, I hear them coming back.

(SLUMP *and* SIMP *come back into the room.*)

SLUMP : There I have everything, my wallet, my compasses, my slide-rule—right, everything is here.
DUMP : You are very busy. What are you building now ?
SLUMP : I am laying gas mains. They are to go

under the Market Hall. They are 20 feet under the pavement. I have forty workmen working, and six steam-dredges digging. When I see them dig I want to shout, "Ha ha! Dig harder! Dig harder!" Do you like steam-shovels?

DUMP : No, they make a noise.

SLUMP : I like noise. It makes my veins tingle. Don't you like it?

DUMP : No. It closes my ducts. I don't like it.

SLUMP : I do. This morning we are to explode dynamite to blow out the boulders. When it explodes, I like to shout, "Ha! That was a good one!" Don't you like dynamite?

DUMP : No, it oscillates my diaphragm.

SLUMP : Ha! You should learn to like it. Look! here are sticks of it; like shaving-sticks, aren't they? (*He takes from his pockets some short sticks of dynamite.*)

VAMP : Don't speak so roughly. It is bad for Dump. It will make him cough.

(DUMP *coughs.*)

VAMP : You see. Come away, Dump; come into the conservatory. I have a lovely eschscholtzia that I want to show you.

(VAMP *and* DUMP *go out.*)

Round Three is now complete. It is meant to

show that Slump, the sub-contractor, is a man of terrible driving-power. He is filled with the " drang " of life. You have to call this " drang " simply " drang," because in English we don't have it. It means something the same as " pep," but not quite. " Pep " is intellectual; " drang " is bodily. It means, as all the critics of the play point out, that Slump represents the up-surge of elemental forces.

SLUMP (*calling*) : Now then, Simp; my hat, my stick, and a glass of sprott. Where are you ?

SIMP : I am coming, master.

> (SIMP *comes in with a hat and stick, and with a glass of sprott in her hand.*)

SLUMP : Ha, give it to me ! I like my sprott. It makes my eyes bulge. (*He drinks greedily.*)

SIMP : You shouldn't drink so fast.

SLUMP : I like to drink fast. It inflates me. Ha ! (*He finishes the glass and puts it aside.*)

SLUMP : Ha ! That's good. You're a pretty girl.

SIMP : Oh !

SLUMP : Come and give me a kiss.

SIMP : No.

SLUMP : Yes, you shall. (*He takes hold of Simp and draws her towards him.*)

SIMP : No.

SLUMP : Yes, I say. (*He kisses* SIMP *greedily three or four times.*) There !

SIMP : You shouldn't kiss me.

SLUMP : Why not ?

SIMP : I have an hereditary taint.

SLUMP (*aghast*) : What ?

SIMP : I have an hereditary taint. My grandmother died of appendicitis.

SLUMP (*staggering back, his hand to his brow*) : Appendicitis !

SIMP : Yes, look, I have the marks of it.

> (SIMP *raises her sleeve and shows a round red mark on her wrist.*)

SLUMP : Great heavens ! Sprott ! Give me some more sprott ! (*He stands staring in front of him, while* SIMP *fetches another glass of sprott. He drinks it eagerly.*)

SIMP : How do you feel now ?

SLUMP : Bad. There are specks dancing in front of my eyes. What does it mean ?

SIMP : Appendicitis.

SLUMP : I am doomed ! Give me more sprott. Appendicitis ! Sprott. Appendicitis !

. . . . .

The action of the play pauses here a moment to let the audience appreciate the full measure of retribution that has fallen upon Slump for kissing a Swedish housemaid. Slump has sunk into a chair,

and sits with his eyes staring in front of him. Simp
stands looking at him unconcerned. Vamp and
Dump come back.

VAMP : Good heavens ! What is the matter ?

DUMP : What is it ?

SIMP : I don't know. I don't think he is well.

SLUMP (*beginning to bark like a dog*) : Wow ! Wow !

VAMP : No, he is not well.

DUMP : He is hardly himself.

SLUMP : Bow ! Wow !

VAMP : I should say that he is ill.

DUMP : Yes, he seems poorly.

SLUMP : Wow !

VAMP : He appears in poor health.

DUMP : Yes, he looks out of sorts.

> (SLUMP *takes the stick of dynamite out
> of his pocket and begins to eat it.*)

VAMP : What is he doing now ?

DUMP : I think he is eating dynamite.

VAMP : Will it hurt him ?

DUMP : Yes, presently.

VAMP : In what particular way ?

DUMP : After the warmth of his body warms it,
he will explode.

VAMP : How curious ! How warm will it have to
be ?

DUMP : About 90 degrees. It will take about a

minute for each degree. He will explode in twelve minutes.

VAMP : Is it wise to stay near him ?

DUMP : No, it is highly imprudent. We had better go. Simp had better gather up your things. We will go together. It is scarcely wise to linger.

VAMP : No, let us hasten.

SLUMP : Wow ! Wow !

· · · · ·

The curtain falls, leaving, as usual after an Ibsen play, a profound problem stated but not solved.

VI—The Historic Drama

AFTER all, there is nothing like the Historic Drama. Say what you will about moving pictures or high-speed vaudeville, they never have the same air and class to them. For me, as soon as I see upon the programme "A tucket sounds," I am all attention; and when it says "Enter Queen Elizabeth to the sound of Hoboes" I am thrilled. What does it matter if the Queen's attendants seem to speak as if they came from Yonkers? There is dignity about it, all the same. When you have, moving in front of you on the stage, people of the class of Louis Quatorze, Henry Quinze, Oliver Cromwell, and Mary of Roumania, you feel somehow as if they were distinctly superior to such characters as Big-hearted Jim, and Shifty Pete, and Meg of the Bowery, and Inspector Corcoran. Perhaps they are.

But of all the characters that walk upon the stage, commend me to Napoleon. What I don't know about that man's life, from seeing him on the boards, is not worth discussing. I have only to close my eyes and I can see him before me as depicted by our greatest actors, with his one lock of hair and his forehead like a door - knob, his melancholy eyes painted black and yellow underneath. And as for his family life, his relations with Josephine, his dealings with the Countess Skandaliska, I could write it all down if it was lost.

There is something about that man—I don't mind admitting it—that holds me. And he exercises the same fascination over all our great actors. About once in every ten years some one of them, intoxicated by success, decides that he wants to be Napoleon. It is a thing that happens to all of them. It is something in their brain that breaks.

Every time that this happens, a new Napoleonic play is produced. That is, it is called *new*, but it is really the same old play over again. The title is always entirely new, but that is because it is a convention that the title of a Napoleon play is never a straight-out statement of what it means, such as *Napoleon, Emperor of France,* or *Napoleon and Josephine.* It is called, let us say, *Quinze Pour Cent,* or *Mille Fois Non,* or *Des Deux Choses L'Une*— that sort of thing. And, after it is named, it is always strung together in the same way, and it is always done in little fits and starts that have no real connection with one another, but are meant to show Napoleon at all the familiar angles. In fact, here is how it goes :

DES DEUX CHOSES L'UNE :

A DRAMA OF THE FIRST EMPIRE

(*Adapted from the French of Dumas, Sardou, Hugo, Racine, Corneille, and all others who ever wrote of Napoleon.*)

The opening part of the play is intended to show the extraordinary fidelity towards the Emperor on the part of the Marshals of France whom he had created.

SCENE I

The Ballroom of the Palace of the Tuileries

Standing around are ladies in Directoire dresses, brilliant as rainbows. Upright beside them are the Marshals of France. There is music and a buzz of conversation.

Enter Napoleon, followed by Talleyrand, all in black, and two secretaries carrying boxes. There is silence. The Emperor seats himself at a little table. The secretaries place on it two black dispatch boxes.

THE EMPEROR speaks : " Marshal Junot ! "

The Marshal steps forward and salutes.

THE EMPEROR : " Marshal, I have heard strange rumours and doubts about your fidelity. I wish to test it. I have here " (*he opens one of the boxes*) " a vial of poison. Here, drink it."

JUNOT : " With pleasure, Sire."

Junot drinks the poison and stands to attention.

THE EMPEROR : " Go over there, and stand beside the Countess de la Polissonerie till you die."

JUNOT (*saluting*) : " With pleasure, Sire."

NAPOLEON (*turning to another*) : " Marshal Berthier ! "

" Here, Sire."

Berthier steps out in front of the Emperor.

THE EMPEROR (*rising*) : " Ha ha ! Is it you ? " (*He reaches up and pinches Berthier's ear.*) " *Vieux paquet de linge !* "

Berthier looks delighted. It is amazing what a French Marshal will do for you if you pinch his ear. At least, it is a tradition of the stage. In these scenes Napoleon always pinched the Marshals' ears and called them, " *Vieux paquet de linge*," etc.

The Emperor turns stern in a moment.

" Marshal Berthier ! "

" Sire."

" Are you devoted to my person ? "

" Sire, you have but to put me to the test."

" Very well. Here, Marshal Berthier " (*Napoleon reaches into the box*), " is a poisoned dog-biscuit. Eat it."

BERTHIER (*saluting*) : " With pleasure, Sire. It is excellent."

NAPOLEON : " Very good, *Mon Vieux trait d'union*. Now go and talk to the Duchesse de la Rôtisserie till you die."

Berthier bows low.

THE EMPEROR : " Marshal Lannes ! You look pale. Here is a veal chop. It is full of arsenic. Eat it."

Marshal Lannes bows in silence, and swallows the chop in one bite.

The Emperor then gives a packet of prussic acid to Marshal Soult, one pill each to Marshal Duroc and Augereau, and then suddenly he rises and stamps his foot.

" No, Talleyrand ; no ! The farce is finished ! I can play it no longer. Look, *les braves enfants* ! They have eaten poison for me. *Ah non, mes amis, mes vieux*. Reassure yourselves. You are not to die. See, the poison was in the other box."

TALLEYRAND (*shrugging his shoulders*) : " If your Majesty insists on spoiling everything——"

NAPOLEON : " Yes, yes ; these brave fellows could not betray me. Come, Berthier ; come, Junot ; come, and let us cry together. . . ."

The Emperor and his Marshals all gather in a group, sobbing convulsively and pulling one another's ears.

But one must not think that the Imperial Court was all sentiment. Ah no! The great brain of the Emperor could be turned in a moment to other concerns, and focused into a single point of concentrated efficiency. As witness:

Scene II

Showing how Napoleon used to dictate a Letter, carry on a Battle, and Revealing Business Efficiency at the Acme

Napoleon in a room in a château, announced to be somewhere near a battle, striding up and down, dictating a letter with his hat on. On the stage the great Emperor always dictates through his hat. A secretary sitting at a table is vainly trying to keep pace with the rush of words.

"Now, are you ready, de Meneval? Have you written that last sentence?"

De Meneval (*writing desperately*): "In a moment, Sire; in a moment."

"Imbecile! Write this then: 'The Prefect of Lyons is ordered to gather all possible cannon for the defence of Toulon . . . is reminded that there are six cannon on the ramparts of Lyons which he has apparently forgotten. The Emperor orders him to pass them forward at once.' Have you written that, imbecile ? "

" In a moment, Sire ; in a moment."

" ' To have them forwarded to Toulon. He is reminded that there are six more in the back garden of the Ministry of the Marine, and two put away in the basement of the Methodist Church.' "

The Secretary collapses. Napoleon stamps his foot. A terrible-looking Turkish attendant, Marmalade the Mameluke, comes in and drags him out by the collar, and then drags in another secretary and props him up in a chair, where he at once commences to write furiously.

Napoleon never stops dictating :

" ' There are two more cannons in the garage of the Prefect of Police. One has a little piece knocked out of the breech——' "

THE SECRETARY (*pausing in surprise*) : " *Mon Dieu !* "

THE EMPEROR : " Eh, what, *mon enfant* ; what surprises you ? "

" Ah, Sire, it is too wonderful. How can you tell that a piece is out of the breeches ? "

NAPOLEON (*pinching his ear*) : " Ha ! You think me wonderful ! "

THE SECRETARY : " I do."

NAPOLEON (*pulling his hair*): " I am. And my cannon ! I know them all. That one with the piece knocked out of the breech, shall I tell you how I know it ? "

THE SECRETARY : " Ah, Sire, you——"

Marmalade the Mameluke comes in and salaams to the ground.

THE EMPEROR : " Well, what is it ? *Vieux fromage de cuir !* "

The Mameluke gurgles about a pint of Turkish.

THE EMPEROR : " Ha ! Bring her in. . . . You may go. You, Marmalade, stand after she enters, stand behind that curtain, so—your scimitar, so— if I stamp my left foot—you understand."

MARMALADE (*with a salaam*) : " Zakouski, Anchovi."

EMPEROR : " Good. Show her in."

There enters with a rush the beautiful half-Polish Countess Skandaliska. She throws herself at the Emperor's feet.

" Sire, Sire ! My husband. I crave his life."

NAPOLEON (*taking her by the chin and speaking coldly*) : " You are very beautiful."

" Sire ! My husband. I ask his life. He is under order to be shot this morning."

THE EMPEROR (*coldly*) : " Let me feel your ears."

" Ah, Sire ! In pity, I beg you for his life."

THE EMPEROR (*absently*) : " You have nice fat arms. Let me pinch them."

" Sire ! My husband. . . ."

THE EMPEROR (*suddenly changing his tone*) : " Yes, your husband. Did you think I did not know ? I have it here."

He turns his back on the Countess, picks up a document from the table, and reads :

" ' Scratchitoff Skandalisko, Count of Poland, Baron of Lithuania, Colonel of the Fifth Lancers, reported by the Imperial Police as in the pay of the Czar of Russia.' Ha! Did you think I did not know that ? "

His back is still turned. The Countess is standing upright. Her face is as of stone. Slowly she draws from her bodice a long poniard ; slowly she raises it above the Emperor's back.

Napoleon goes on reading :

" ' . . . Conspired with seven others, since executed, to take the life of the Emperor, and now this 5th day of September . . .' "

The Countess has raised the poniard to its height. As she is about to stab the Emperor, he taps slightly with his foot. Marmalade the Mameluke has flung aside the curtain and grasps the Countess from behind by both wrists. The poniard rattles to the floor. The Emperor turns, and goes on calmly reading the document :

" ' . . . this 5th day of September, pardoned by the clemency of the Emperor and restored to his estates.' "

The Countess, released by Marmalade, falls weeping at the Emperor's feet.

" Ah, Sire, Sire ! you are indeed noble."

NAPOLEON : " Am I not ? Take her out, Marmalade."

The Mameluke bows, takes out the weeping Countess, and returns with a renewed salaam :

THE EMPEROR (*dreamily*) : " We know how to treat them, don't we, old *trognon de chou* ? Let no one disturb that mirror. It may serve us again. And now, bring me a secretary, and I will go on dictating."

In this way did the great Emperor transact more business in a week than most men would get through in a day.

But in this very same play of *Des Deux Choses L'Une* we have to remember that, while all these other things are happening, Napoleon is also fighting a battle.

In fact, hardly is the Countess Skandaliska well off the premises before a military aide-de-camp comes rattling into the room. The Great Brain is in full operation again in a second.

" Ha, Colonel Escargot ! What news ? "

" Bad news, Sire. Marshal Masséna reports the battle is lost."

The Emperor frowns.

" Bad news ? The battle lost ? Do you not know, Colonel Escargot, that I do not permit a battle to be lost ? How long have you been in my service ? Let me see ; you were at Austerlitz ? "

" I was, Sire."

" And you were afterwards in Cantonments at Strasburg ? "

" It is true, Sire."

" I saw you there for five minutes on the afternoon of the 3rd of November of 1810."

" Sire, it is wonderful ! "

" Tut, tut, it is nothing. You were playing dominoes. I remember you had just thrown a double three when I arrived."

COLONEL ESCARGOT (*falling on his knees*) : " Sire, it is too much. You are inspired."

THE EMPEROR (*smiling*) : " Perhaps. But realize, then, that I do not allow a battle to be lost. Get up, *mon vieux bonnet de coton*. Let me pinch your ear. Now then, this battle. Let us see. De Meneval, give me a map."

The Secretary unfolds a vast map on the table. The Emperor stands in deep thought regarding it. Presently he speaks :

" Where is Masséna ? "

Colonel Escargot (*indicating a spot*): "He is here, Sire."

"What is his right resting on?"

"His right, Sire, is extended here. It is endangered."

The Emperor remains a moment in thought.

"How is his centre?"

"His centre is solid."

"And where has he got his rear?"

"His rear, Sire, is resting on a thorn hedge."

The Emperor: "Ha! Ride to Masséna at once. Tell him to haul in his centre and to stick out his rear. The battle will be won in two hours."

Escargot (*saluting*): "Sire. It is wonderful!"

He clatters out.

Napoleon sinks wearily into a chair. His head droops in his hands. "Wonderful!" he broods. "And yet the one thing of all things that I want to do, I can't do."

Indeed, the man is really up against it. He can remember cannons and win battles and tell Masséna where to put his rear, but, when it comes to Josephine, he is no better than the rest of us.

The Emperor rings the bell.

De Meneval comes in.

"De Meneval, listen. I have taken a decision. I am going to divorce Josephine."

The Secretary bows.

" Go to her at once, and tell her that she is divorced."

The Secretary bows again.

" If she asks why, say that it is the Emperor's command. You understand ? "

DE MENEVAL : " I do."

" If she tries to come here, do not permit it. Stop her; if need be with your own hands. Tell Marmalade she is not to pass. Tell him to choke her. Tell the guard outside to stop her. Tell them to fire a volley at her. Do you understand ? She is *not* to come."

DE MENEVAL : " Alas, Sire, it is too late ! She is here now. I hear her voice."

One can hear outside the protests of the guards. The Empress Josephine, beautiful and dishevelled and streaming with tears, pushes Marmalade aside with an imperious gesture, and dashes into the room. She speaks :

" Napoleon, what is this ? What does it mean ? Tell me it is not true. You could not dare."

NAPOLEON (*timidly*) : " I think there is some mistake. Not dare what ? "

JOSEPHINE : " To divorce me ! You could not ! You would not ! Ah, heartless one, you could not do it."

She falls upon Napoleon's neck, weeping convulsively.

136

THE EMPEROR : " Josephine, there has been a delusion, a misunderstanding. Of course I would not divorce you. Who dares hint at such a thing ? "

JOSEPHINE : " Outside, in the waiting-room, in the court, they are all saying it."

NAPOLEON : " Ha ! Let them dare ! They shall answer with their heads."

JOSEPHINE : " Ah, now, you are my own dear Napoleon. Let me fold you in my arms. Let me kiss you on the top of the head."

She hugs and kisses the Emperor with enthusiasm.

NAPOLEON : " Ah, Josephine, how much I love you ! "

A voice is heard without. Colonel Escargot enters rapidly. He is deadly pale, but has a triumphant look on his face. He salutes.

" Sire, everything is saved."

NAPOLEON : " Ah ! So the battle was not lost after all."

" No, Sire ; your orders were sent by semaphore telegraph. Masséna withdrew his rear and thrust out his centre. A panic broke out in the ranks of the enemy."

" Ha ! The enemy ? Who are they ? "

" We are not sure. We think Russians. But at least, Sire, they are fleeing in all directions. Masséna is in pursuit. The day is ours."

The Emperor : " It is well. But you, Colonel Escargot, you are wounded."

The Colonel (*faintly*) : " No, Sire ; not wounded."

Napoleon : " But yes."

Colonel Escargot : " Not wounded, Sire ; killed. I have a bullet through my heart."

He sinks down on the carpet.

The Emperor bends over him.

Escargot (*feebly*) : " Vive l'Empereur ! "

He dies.

Napoleon (*standing for a moment and looking at the body of Colonel Escargot*) : " Alas, Josephine, all my victories cannot give me back the life of one brave man. I might have known it at the start."

He remains in reflection.

" I should have chosen at the beginning. Tranquillity or conquest, greatness or happiness— *Des Deux Choses L'Une.*"

And, as he says that, the curtain slowly sinks upon the brooding Emperor.

The play is over. In fact, there is no need to go on with it. Now that the audience know why it is called *Des Deux Choses L'Une*, there is no good going any further. All that is now needed is the usual Transfiguration Scene, thus :

Napoleon, dying at St. Helena, seen in a half-

light with a vast net curtain across the stage, and
a dim background of storm, thunder, and the armies
of the dead—

That, with a little rumbling of cannon—the
distant rolling of a South Atlantic storm—

—And then—the pomp has passed—turn up the
lamps and let the *matinée* audience out into the
daylight.

.   .   .   .   .

But we must not suppose for a minute that French
history has any monopoly of dramatic interest. Oh
dear, no. We have recently discovered that right
here, on the North American continent, there is
material teeming with dramatic interest. Any
quantity of it. In fact, it begins at the very start
of our history and goes right on. Consider the
aboriginal Indian ; what a figure for tragedy ! Few
people, perhaps, realize that no less than seventeen
first-class tragedies, each as good as Shakespeare's,
and all in blank verse, have been written about the
Indians. They have to be in blank verse. There
was something about the primitive Indian that
invited it. It was the real way to express him.

Unfortunately these Indian tragedies cannot be
produced on the stage. They are ahead of the
age. The managers to whom they have been sub-
mitted say that as yet there is no stage suitable for

them, and no actors capable of acting them, and no spectators capable of sitting for them.

METTAWAMKEAG

An Indian Tragedy

The scene is laid on the shores of Lake Mettawamkeag, near the junction of the Petticodiac and the Passamoquidiac Rivers.   The sun is rising.

Enter :

> Areopagitica, *an Indian Chief.*
> The Encyclopedia, *a brave of the Appendixes.*
> Pilaffe de Volaille, *a French Coureur des bois.*

Areopagitica :

> "Hail, vernal sun, that thus with trailing beam
> Illuminates with gold the flaming east ;
> Hail, too, cerulean sky, that touched with fire
> Expels th' accumulate cloud of vanished night."

The Encyclopedia : "Hail ! Oh, hail ! "
Pilaffe de Volaille : "Hêle ! Oh, hêle ! "
Areopagitica :

> "All nature seems to leap with morn to song,

Tempting to gladness the awakening bird ;
E'en the dark cedar feels the gladsome
    hour,
And the light larch pulsates in every frond.
Who art thou ?   Whence ?   And whither
    goest thou ? "

PILAFFE DE VOLAILLE :

 " Thrice three revolving suns have waxed
    and waned
Since first I wended hither from afar,
Nor knowing not, nor caring aught, if
    here or there.
Who am I ?   One that is.   Whence come
    I ?   From beyond
The restless main whose hyperboreal tide
Laves coast and climes unknown ;   O
    Chief, to thy sagacity,
        From France I came."

AREOPAGITICA : " Hail ! "

(*What Pilaffe de Volaille means is that he has been
out here for nine years and lives near Mettawamkeag.
But there is such a size and feeling about this other
way of saying it, that it seems a shame that dramas
of this kind can't be acted.*)

After they have all said " Oh, hail ! " and " Oh,
hêle ! " as many times as is necessary, Areopagitica
and The Encyclopedia take Pilaffe de Volaille to
the Lodge of the Appendixes.   There he is enter-

tained on Hot Dog.   And there he meets Sparkling Soda Water, the daughter of Areopagitica.

After the feast the two wander out into the moonlight together beside the waterfall.   Love steals into their hearts.

PILAFFE DE VOLAILLE (*invoking the moon*) :

"Thou silver orb, whose incandescent face
Smiles on the bosom of the turgid flood,
Look deep into mine heart and search if aught
Less pure than thy white beam inspires its love !
Soda, be mine ! "

SODA WATER speaks :

"Alas ! What words are these ? What thought is this ?
Thy meaning what ? Unskilled to know,
My simple words can find no answer to the heart's appeal ;
Where am I at ? "

PILAFFE DE VOLAILLE : " Flee with me."

SODA WATER : " Alas ! "

PILAFFE : " Flee."

SODA WATER (*invoking the constellations of the Zodiac*) :

"Ye glimmering lights, that from the Milky Way
To the tall zenith of the utmost pole

> Illume the vault of heaven, and indicate
> The inclination of the axis of the earth,
> Showing sidereal time and the mean
>   measurement
> Of the earth's parallax,
>   Help me ! "

PILAFFE DE VOLAILLE (*in despair*) : " Oh, hêle ! "

Both the lovers know that their tragic love is hopeless. For them, marriage is out of the question. De Volaille is sprung from an old French family, with eight quarters of noble birth—a high average even at a time when most people were well born. He cannot ally himself with anything less white than himself. On the other hand, Laughing Soda knows that, after the customs of her time, her father has pledged her hand to The Encyclopedia. She cannot marry a pale face.

Thus what might have been a happy marriage is queered from the start. Each is too well-born to stoop to the other. This often happens.

Standing thus in the moonlight beside the waterfall, the lovers are surprised by Areopagitica and The Encyclopedia. In desapir, Laughing Soda leaps into the flood. The noble Encyclopedia plunges headlong after her into the boiling water, and is boiled. De Volaille flees.

Areopagitica vows vengeance. Staining himself

with grape juice, he declares a war of extermination against the white race. The camp of the French is surprised in a night attack. Pilaffe de Volaille, fighting with the courage of his race, is pierced with an Indian arrow. He expires on the spot, having just time before he dies to prophesy in blank verse the future greatness of the United States.

Areopagitica, standing among the charred ruins of the stockaded fort and gazing upon the faces of the dead, invokes the Nebular Hypothesis, and prophesies clearly the League of Nations.

The same dramatic possibilities seem to crop up all through American history, from Christopher Columbus to President Harding.

But to see the thing at its height it is better to skip about three hundred years in one hop, and come down to what is perhaps the greatest epic period in American history, the era of the Civil War.

This great event has been portrayed so often in the drama and the moving pictures that everybody knows just how it is dealt with. It is generally put on under some such title as *The Making of the Nation*, or *The Welding of the Nation*, or *The Riveting of the Nation*—or *The Hammering*, or *The Plastering*—in short, a metaphor taken from the building and contracting trades. Compare this :

FORGING THE FIFTEENTH AMENDMENT

A Drama of the Civil War

The scene is laid in the Council-room of the White House. There are present Abraham Lincoln, Seward, Staunton, Artemus Ward, and the other members of the Cabinet.

Lincoln (*speaking very gravely*) : " Mr. Secretary, what news have you from the Army of the Potomac ? "

Staunton : " Mr. President, the news is bad. General Halleck has been driven across the Rappahannock, General Pope has been driven across the Roanoke, and General Burnside has been driven across the Pamunkey."

Lincoln (*with quiet humour*) : " And has anybody been driven across the Chickahominy ? "

Staunton : " Not yet."

Lincoln : " Then it might be worse. Let me tell you a funny story that I heard ten years ago."

Seward (*with ill-disguised impatience*) : " Mr. President, this is no time for telling stories ten years old."

Lincoln (*wearily*) : " Perhaps not. In that case, fetch me the Constitution of the United States."

The Constitution is brought and is spread out

145

on the table, in front of them. They bend over it anxiously.

LINCOLN (*with deep emotion*) : " What do you make of it ? "

STAUNTON : " It seems to me, from this, that all men are free and equal."

SEWARD (*gravely*) : " And that the power of Congress extends to the regulation of commerce between the States, with foreign States, and with Indian Tribes."

LINCOLN (*thoughtfully*) : " The price of liberty is eternal vigilance."

(In the printed text of the play there is a note here to the effect that Lincoln did not on this particular occasion use this particular phrase. Indeed, it was said by some one else on some other occasion. But it is such a good thing for anyone to say on any occasion, that it is the highest dramatic art to use it.)

LINCOLN (*standing up from the table to his full height and speaking as one who looks into the future*) : " Gentlemen, I am prepared to sacrifice any part of this Constitution to save the whole of it, or to sacrifice the whole of it to save any part of it ; but what I will not do is to sacrifice all of it to save none of it."

There is a murmur of applause. But at this very moment a messenger dashes in :

" Mr. President, telegraphic news from the seat of war ! General Grant has been pushed over the Chickahominy ! "

LINCOLN : Pushed backwards or pushed forwards ? "

THE MESSENGER : " Forwards."

LINCOLN (*gravely*) : " Gentlemen, the Union is safe."

VII—The Russian Drama—(A) Old Style

BASILISK VANGOROD

THIS is the kind of play that used to deal with dear old Russia when there was nothing more dangerous there than the knout, and exile to Siberia, and the salt mines, and nihilists with black whiskers, and bombs as large as a plum pudding. The good old place is changed now. Life there, from what I can gather at a distance of six thousand miles—which is all I propose to gather—seems in some way—how shall I say it ?—restrained, what one might call unhomelike. But in the dear old days there was a freedom and a space about Russia which reflected itself in the drama.

Here is the sort of thing that we used to gaze at spellbound in the middle eighties :

SCENE

Siberia : A Post-Station

In the old days there was always a peculiar touch
about the very word " Siberia "—a sort of thrill, or
chill, that you couldn't get elsewhere. It suggested
great empty spaces, a vast plain of snow broken
with dark pine woods, and moujiks with long whips
driving one-horse tarantulas over the frozen surface
of the endless samovar. Everywhere was the tunga
tufted here and there with vodka.

At intervals in the snow was a post-house—a rude
building made of logs with outhouses for shelter ng
exiles in. Everywhere there were prisoners and
exiles, wandering up and down in little strings.
They never got anywhere that I know of. They
were just driven from play to play and from story
to story. Among the prisoners were nihilists with
bombs, girls who had lost their husbands, anarchists,
Tartars—in fact, a varied and cheerful lot.

The opening scene was always laid—

Inside the Post-House

It is a long room, with a fire burning at the side,
a few rough chairs and tables ; only one person
is in it, a moujik or sort of peasant servant, in a
tattered hat and a chewed-up fur coat.

The door opens with a burst of paper snow, and
in stride two Russian officers. They go to the fire
and stick their hands out towards its warmth.

" It's a cold night, Petroff."

" A cold night, Dimitri Dimitrivitch, but not so cold as in the outshed where the exiles are, ha ha ! "

Both officers laugh heartily.

This is a first-class Russian jest.

" One of the dogs," says Petroff, expanding his back to the fire, " fell in the snow on the march to-day."

" And what did you do, Dimitri ? "

" I ordered him a touch of the knout. I think the dog died where he fell, ha ha ! Ha ha ! "

Both laugh heartily again.

Petroff turns to the peasant servant.

" Here, dog ; bring vodka ! "

" At once, Excellence, at once." The moujik fumbles in a cupboard and brings a bottle and glasses.

Both officers drink.

" To the Czar, Petroff ! "

" Dimitri, to the Czar ! "

A Russian soldier with a gun and a bayonet about two feet long steps in and salutes.

" Excellence, a woman is outside."

" A woman ? Ha ! What like of woman, Ivan ? "

" Excellence, a young woman."

" A young woman ! Ha ! Ha ha ha ! "

The two officers stride up and down repeating,

" A young woman, ha ! Bring her in." It is plain that they mean to eat her.

The soldier salutes and goes out and returns in a moment, dragging in a girl by the wrist.

This is Nitnitska Nitouscha, and she is looking for her father. She is very beautiful, with her hair in two braids and a bright-coloured schapska over her head and shoulders.

Petroff grabs her by the wrists and twists her arm twice round and says : " Ha ha ! The girl is not ill to look at, Dimitri ; and what want you here, pretty one ? "

NITNITSKA : " I am seeking my father."

Petroff gives her arm two more turns, and says :

" Your father ? "

" Yes, he is among the prisoners."

Both officers laugh. " Among the prisoners, ha ha ! "

Dimitri slips up to the girl and twists her other wrist.

" And what might his name be, tell me that."

Petroff takes her by the ear and twists it, and says :

" Yes, tell us that."

" His name is written here on this paper, and he is an old man, a very old man ; he is too feeble to walk with the prisoners."

Dimitri laughs brutally. " So ! He is too feeble

to walk ?   In that case we can help him with the knout, ha ha ! "

He takes the girl by the other ear and turns it twice round.

" And what would you with your father ? "

" I want his freedom."

Both officers laugh.   " His freedom, ha ha ! "

" His freedom.   See, on this paper, I have an order for his freedom signed by the Czar himself."

" By the Czar ? "

Both officers fall back from the girl, repeating, " By the Czar ? "

" Yes, there it is on the paper."

Nitnitska hands over a paper.   Petroff takes it and reads it aloud, scowling :

" By command of His Imperial Highness and in accord with the signed order transmitted herewith, you are commanded to release into liberty the person of Vladimir Ilyitch."

Petroff, with a start, repeats the name, " Vladimir Ilyitch ! "

Nitnitska : " Yes, yes ; my father, Vladimir Ilyitch ! "

Petroff : " Dimitri, a word in your ear."

They step aside.

" Vladimir Ilyitch ! That dog that was struck down with the knout and left for dead——"

Dimitri nods. " That was his name."

PETROFF : " The girl must never leave here alive."

DIMITRI : " No, we must choke her."

PETROFF (*turning towards Nitnitska*) : " Girl, we are going to choke you."

NITNITSKA : " Cowards ! " She has set her back against the wall near the window and looks at them defiantly. " If you dare to choke me, you shall die. Look ! " She draws forth from her dress a silver whistle on a chain. " I have but to blow upon this whistle and Basilisk Vangorod and his Tartars will fall upon the post."

PETROFF : " Seize her ! "

They rush at her. Nitnitska blows a long blast on the silver whistle. Petroff and Dimitri start to choke her, both together, but before they get her more than half choked there is sudden outbreak of gun-fire outside.

Ivan, the sentinel, rushes in.

" Excellence, the post is attacked by Tartars ! "

PETROFF (*letting go the girl*) : " Call all the guards ! Every man to his post ! "

The guards—three of them—rush in and begin firing through the windows. There is a tremendous quantity of firing outside. Presently a full-sized explosion blows in the door. In rushes Basilisk Vangorod, followed by his whole Tartar Army— four of them. The Russian guards are hopelessly outnumbered—four to three. They lay down their arms. Basilisk Vangorod rushes at Petroff and Dimitri, and fights them both in a sword combat which circles round the stage so that everybody can see a piece of it. As it concludes, he kills Dimitri and Petroff, clasps Nitnitska in his arms, calls in her father (who is outside, and not dead) and stands in the middle of the stage waving his sword, and says, " For the Freedom of Russia ! Long live the Czar ! "

And the curtain falls.

The Russian Drama—(B) *New Style*

DAMNED SOULS

(A bright little tragedy of Russian home life, written with a little assistance by Maxim Gherkin, Shootitoff, Dustanashej, and a few men like that.)

SCENE.—AN UNDERGROUND LODGING IN PINSK

WATER EXUDES FROM THE WALLS : DIM DAYLIGHT COMES THROUGH A HALF-WINDOW. THERE IS A CRAZY TABLE IN THE MIDDLE OF THE ROOM, SOME CRAZY CHAIRS, A CRAZY STOVE, ON WHICH IS A SAMOVAR WITH SOME CRAZY TEA. IN A CORNER OF THE ROOM IS A LOW-VAULTED DOOR, WHICH OPENS ON RICKETY STAIRS DESCENDING TO A BLACK CELLAR.

THE CAST OF (WANT OF) CHARACTERS

STYLIPIN	*A Thief.*
YATSCHSCHA	*His Wife.*
PATCH	*An Imbecile.*
HOOTCH	*A Homicidal Maniac.*
ITCH	*A Paragoric.*

All these are in the room already when the play begins. Later, the following further want of characters come in, namely :

PRAVDA (aged eighty) . .	*An Immoral Woman.*
PRYBILOFF	*A Murderer.*

Their entry is kept until a little later to brighten things up in case they get dull.

When the curtain rises, Itch, the paragoric, is lying on a truckle-bed, under dirty bedclothes, in a corner of the room. He is evidently dying by inches, in fact, by centimetres; his feet are already ossified. In fact, he is quite sick.

Patch, the imbecile, is making faces at himself in a broken looking-glass. Hootch, the homicidal maniac, is sharpening a butcher's knife. Stylipin and Yatschscha are drinking vodka out of dirty glasses at the crazy table. In other words, it's a regular Russian home scene.

ITCH (*sitting up in bed*): "I'm hungry."

STYLIPIN: "Shut up."

ITCH: "Give me some water, I'm thirsty."

STYLIPIN: "Shut up, or I'll choke you."

YATSCHSCHA: That's right. Choke him." (*Aside.*) "He has money under his bed, in the mattress. I saw it yesterday. Choke him and take it."

STYLIPIN (*aside*): "Later."

ITCH: "Mother Pravda, Mother Pravda, give me some food!"

STYLIPIN: "Shut up, I say. She's out. Mother Pravda is out."

ITCH: "I'm dying."

THE IMBECILE (*with sudden laughter*): "He's dying! Ha ha! Isn't he lucky? He's dying!"

Itch falls back on his bed. There is a gurgling in his throat. Nobody pays any more attention to him.

STYLIPIN (*turning to Yatschscha*) : " Where is that money you brought in from the street ? "

YATSCHSCHA : "I brought no money from the street."

STYLIPIN : " You're lying, you foul hussy. Give it me, or I'll beat you ! "

He picks up a stick.

PATCH, the idiot (*clapping his hands with insane laughter*) : " Ha ha ! Beat her ! That's right, beat her ! "

STYLIPIN : " Give me the money or I'll choke you."

He takes Yatschscha by the throat and begins to choke her. Strange cries come from her. The idiot capers and chuckles.

" Choke her ! That's it, choke her ! "

HOOTCH, the homicidal maniac : " Stop your accursed noise. Do you want to bring the whole street in on us ? Stop, I say ; there's some one coming down the steps."

All are still a moment, their motions arrested as they stand. Only the gurgling noise is still heard from the throat of Itch, the paragoric.

.   .   .   .   .

This opening part of the play is intended to

develop that atmosphere of cheerfulness and comfort which surrounds the Russian drama of to-day. It can, if need be, be prolonged still more with little vignettes of choking, poisoning, and knifing. But there should be at least enough of it to develop the temperamental aspect of the Russian stage.

. . . . .

STYLIPIN : " Yes, there's some one coming down the steps. Quiet, I say ! "

There is a beating at the chained door.

Stylipin goes to the door. He motions for silence, his hand upon the chain. He calls :

" Who's there ? "

" It is I. Open the door."

" It's Mother Pravda. Are you alone, little mother ? "

" No, one is with me. It is all right. Open."

Stylipin opens the door. Mother Pravda enters ; she is followed by Prybiloff, the murderer. His face is like ashes. His eyes wander. He is afraid.

" Who has she got ? What is it ? Who is she bringing ? "

" This is Prybiloff, children. He has done a murder."

HOOTCH, the homicidal maniac : " Aha ! A murderer ! With a knife, was it, brother ? With a knife ? A knife like this ? " His eyes glisten.

Prybiloff goes and sits down. He is shaking.

158

" I don't know. It was dark."

" And you struck him down in the dark ? Eh, brother, in the dark ? Was there blood ? Tell me if there was blood ? "

PRYBILOFF (*his face in his hands*) : " I don't know, I didn't see."

THE IMBECILE (*going near him*) : "Don't cry, little brother."

YATSCHSCHA (*taking her husband aside*) : " Listen, there is money in his pocket—coins, real money. I heard it jingle in his pocket."

STYLIPIN : " I know it. I heard it too. Who did he kill, Mother Pravda ? "

PRAVDA : " He killed a commissary. The people are after him in the streets. They are searching. They want to burn him. Listen ! "

There is heard a confused sound of shouting and running feet as from the streets outside.

PRYBILOFF (*lifting his head, his hands clenched on the table*) : " They're coming ! "

PRAVDA : " Have no fear. Look, come with me. There is a cellar below here. I'll put you there. Come."

She leads him towards the low-vaulted door in the corner.

THE IMBECILE : " She is taking him below ! Ha ha ! Don't go, brother, it's too good a jest. Don't let her take you."

STYLIPIN and HOOTCH : "Shut up, fool, shut up——"

Mother Pravda opens the door, leads Prybiloff down the dark steps. The sound of shouting has died away. Pravda's voice can be heard down below : "This way, little brother. There, I will make a light."

One can see the gleam of yellow candlelight through the door.

STYLIPIN (to Hootch) : "Shall we go down ?"

HOOTCH : "Let her do it alone."

STYLIPIN : "No, no, I'm going down. I don't trust her. She'll take more than her share."

HOOTCH : "All right. Here, take the spade with us. Better finish the job."

STYLIPIN (to Yatschscha) : "Wait here. Keep the door chained. Let no one in. Come on, Hootch."

They go through the door down the steps. There is a confused sound of voices from below. Then the sudden noise of a scuffle, one strange cry, and silence.

THE IMBECILE (*with laughter*) : "Ha ha ! He *would* go ! Like the others ! Now they will bury him down there with the shovels ; oh, what fun ! Do you hear, little brother ; what a rare joke !"

He goes over to Itch's bed : "Do you hear, brother, a rare joke. He doesn't answer ! "

YATSCHSCHA (*looking at* ITCH *callously*) : "He can't answer. He is dead."

A voice calls from below.

" Are you there, Yatschscha ? Bring the vodka.
The work is hard."

YATSCHSCHA : " One minute, one minute." She
takes from her pocket a little phial with green
liquid in it——

.   .   .   .   .

But there, there. What's the use of going on
with it. The full temperamentality of the thing
has been developed by this time. What happens is
that Yatschscha puts poison in the vodka. And
when she has done that she goes out stealthily to
denounce her husband and Hootch to the commissaries of the police. She does this to get the
blood-money offered by the police for Stylipin,
dead or alive. In fact, this is a favourite means of
support in Russia. So Stylipin and Hootch and
dear old Mother Pravda presently come up and
drink the poisoned vodka, and die in contortions.
And when the commissaries of the police, led by
Yatschscha, come in, there is only the idiot, laughing
over all the corpses.

Nice little thing, isn't it ? There is no doubt
that life in Russia has a charm all its own, and that
Russian literature has a tang to it that you don't
get in the duller countries.

VIII—"The Platter of Life"

I OBSERVE that a new controversy has broken out about the moving pictures. Somebody has just calculated that in America twenty million people attend the picture houses every day, and the public is aghast. And even this figure, it seems, doesn't include the Mexicans, the Lower Californians, and the Canadians and the Esquimaux.

It appears also that £50,000,000 of new capital is being put into moving pictures every year—either that or £50,000,000,000. I forget which; but it doesn't matter. It is freely stated that the moving pictures are four-fifths piffle and the other fifth poison ; and that they are made up altogether of sex stuff, sob stuff, crime stuff, and hysteria and vanity all mixed up together.

I do not wish to take any personal part in this controversy. Indeed, as one who has made not one moving picture scenario but hundreds of them, I should feel a delicacy in doing so. But it may be of interest to know just exactly how we scenario-makers make scenarios. Perhaps I may be able to prove that even a moving picture may move on a high plane.

The first thing that a writer has to do to make a scenario is to get a general topic or story. This is absolutely easy. There is no need to invent a new one ; and it is impossible anyway. All the stories were invented long ago.

Open any book of folklore or fairy tales or nursery rhymes, and you can pick them out like plums. You could select "Little Bo Peep," or "Mother Hubbard," or "Jack Spratt," or any of them as the basis. Suppose we take "Jack Spratt."

The original text of the rhyme runs :

" Jack Spratt could eat no fat, his wife could eat no lean,
  And so it was, between them both, they licked the platter clean."

That's the groundwork to begin upon ; the next thing is to find the general name of the picture. That suggests itself at once from the rhyme.

THE PLATTER OF LIFE

or

PARTED AND REUNITED.

(Authorized by the Board of Censors.)

After that it is necessary to work out the descriptive stuff that goes along with the title for advertising purposes. This is where the highest art of

moving-picture-making comes in. It is done more
or less like this :

> HAVE YOU EVER FELT YOUR HUSBAND TURNING
> COLD ?——COLD AS THE UNTASTED BACON
> UPON THE PLATTER ? OR YOU, HAVE YOU
> EVER WATCHED YOUR WIFE GROWING FAT ?
> HAVE YOU SEEN HER EXPAND HOUR BY HOUR ?
> IF SO, YOU MUST NOT MISS THIS VERY NEW
> HEART - THROBBING, PULSE - ACCELERATING
> PICTURE. IN IT YOU WILL SEE AN ÆSTHETIC,
> TEMPERAMENTAL, LEAN-EATING MAN, YOKED
> TO A FULL - BLOODED, DOUBLE - CHESTED
> WOMAN, VIBRATING WITH THE JOY OF
> EATING FAT BY THE POUND. WHAT WILL
> HAPPEN ? CAN THEY DO IT ?

> IT IS A BEAUTIFUL, WHOLESOME PICTURE
> OF MODERN LIFE. THE CLERGY OF ALL
> DENOMINATIONS HAVE COME TO IT IN
> THOUSANDS AND SHED TEARS.

Now the pictures begin to spin, and they show
the familiar interior, called " The Spratt Mansion,"
well known also as " The Anstruther Residence,"
or " The De Kuyper Home." It stands for High
Society, as seen in the movies. It has in it a wooden
butler to take Spratt's coat and stick each time he
goes in and out, and a hundred-dollar housemaid,
much prettier than Mrs. Spratt.

Somewhere in here put in the legend :

JOHN SPRATT, ÆSTHETIC, TEMPERAMENTAL,
A POET, AND A GRADUATE OF OBERLIN
COLLEGE, IS MARRIED TO GLORIA SPRATT,
HIS WIFE.

The pictures ripple on. The Spratts at breakfast. Jack Spratt has a manuscript poem spread in front of him. He keeps raising his eyes to the ceiling and nibbling lean bacon. This means that he is making up poetry. Gloria Spratt is eating fat pork with molasses in it. She comes over to kiss Spratt. He repulses her. She wants to bite his ear. He won't let her. She tries to pick him up and hug him, but he slips out of her arms and darts out of the room.

At this point, the legend is put on the screen :

THIS GREAT BIG, YEARNING, FULL-BLOODED,
OVER-BALLASTED WOMAN IS NOT SATISFIED.
HER LOVE TURNS COLD.

Mrs. Spratt, now cold, writing at a letter table a telegram to a former lover. You can see the address, "William de Bulk, New York," and the message is put right on to the screen to read :

MY MARRIAGE IS A MISTAKE. COME TO ME.

This is the point, I think, at which the clergy begin to weep. But before they have time to

weep much, the scene changes with a sudden flip.
A title is written :

SPRATT, IN HIS STUDY, DICTATES HIS POEM
TO HIS STENOGRAPHER, CLEMENTINA CLICK.

Ha ha ! Do you notice his stenographer, as
thin as a meridian of longitude, and with her hair
in Cleo de Merode forehead-flaps, and with eyes
like a cow ? Something will be doing here.

The gentle girl, as thin as she is good, hangs on
the poet's words.

Then the picture changes again. Arrival of
William de Bulk. You see him buzz up in his
motor. You see the wooden butler take his stick.
Then you see him enter and greet Gloria. William !
How stout you have grown ! He has a big, blue
face like a thug, but he must be all right, because
the writing says :

THE BIG, TRUE-HEARTED MAN HAS COME AT
ONCE TO THE WOMAN HE HAD LOVED.

William takes Gloria Spratt away in his motor.
It is made to look like an elopement, but if you
follow it closely it is all in the same day. It has
to be, or the clergy would stop crying.

" TAKE ME AWAY, WILLIAM. I WANT TO
FORGET. I WANT TO PLUNGE INTO THE
VORTEX OF GAIETY."

He plunges her in. William and Gloria in a restaurant eating beefsteak ; wild scene of gaiety ; Hawaiian orchestra ; wines ; Greek waiters ; gramophones ; all the fierce vortex of Metropolitan life. William tells the story of his life. You can see him do it in side pictures :

"YES, GLORIA, AFTER YOU LEFT ME, I MARRIED. BUT I GREW STOUT, AND MY WIFE ABANDONED ME TO SEEK A MORE INTELLECTUAL LIFE THAN I COULD GIVE HER."

William is seen to bow his head in grief. Then the picture changes back to the Spratt Mansion.

Freed from the pressure of his wife's society, Spratt abandons himself to his poetic dreams.

The picture spins. Spratt (at 10.30) writing a sonnet. Spratt in the garden of the Spratt Mansion (11.30) reading the sonnets to his stenographer. Spratt at lunch with his stenographer, reading the sonnet again. Ease and a tranquil mind are changing him already. At 11.30 he is distinctly stouter than he was. At 1.0 p.m. he is quite fat.

The scene changes. Gloria and William at afternoon tea (4.0 p.m.)

But even in the whirl of gaiety this great big, true-hearted, able-bodied woman cannot forget. She pines.

Pictures of Mrs. Spratt pining. She is losing flesh. At 4.0 p.m. she is far less stout than she was at 3.30. At 4.30 it is still more noticeable.

The picture changes. Spratt with Clementina Click in the garden. He is reading her his sonnet for the tenth time. He is quite stout. Clementina Click shows signs of restlessness. She rises and paces to and fro :

> " MR. SPRATT, DON'T READ IT ANY MORE.
> I HAVE MADE A FATAL MISTAKE. I DO NOT
> CARE FOR POETRY AS I THOUGHT I DID. I
> LEFT THE BEST HUSBAND IN THE WORLD TO
> SEEK THE INTELLECTUAL LIFE. I WANT IT
> NO LONGER."

The picture changes. William and Gloria beside the Duck Pond in Central Park (5.30 p.m.). She is now quite tall and thin :

> " WILLIAM, I HAVE DONE WRONG. EVEN IN
> THIS MAD WORLD OF GAIETY, AMONG THESE
> DUCKS, I CANNOT FORGET. TAKE ME
> HOME."

Concluding scenes. Arrival of the motor at the Spratt Mansion (6.0 p.m. daylight-saving time). Entry of William and Gloria. The Spratts meet. They each weight 150 pounds now. They fall into one another's arms. William and Clementina meet.

They fall into one another's arms. She is his wife.

> " WILLIAM, I HAVE BEEN WRONG. TAKE
> ME BACK."

Mrs. Spratt leads them all to the supper table :

> " COME, WE WILL EAT THE PLATTER CLEAN."

And the picture concludes with the legend :

> AND FROM THE DEAD ASHES OF THEIR PAST
> LIVES THESE RENEWED SOULS LIFT THEM-
> SELVES INTO A HIGHER BEING, WEDNESDAY,
> THURSDAY, AND FRIDAY. ALL THIS WEEK.

(All Rights Reserved.)

IX—"*The Vampire Woman*"
(*As met in the Movies*)

I UNDERSTAND that there is a kind of woman round just now called a Vampire Woman, or a Vamp. I'd like to know her. From all I hear she is just the kind of woman that I think I'd like.

I believe I first noticed her in the moving pictures. In these she wears a shimmering, snaky kind of dress that fits her like onion peel. Personally, I know nothing of dress. In fact, my wife says I never observe it. That is an error. At the right moment, I do. And I must say that that onion-peel effect commands my warmest approval. The Vampire Woman wears nothing on her arms and shoulders. She doesn't need to. And her dress is generally slit up the side a good deal. This allows her freedom of movement. In my opinion she ought to have it. Freedom of movement is a splendid thing.

I don't mean to say that the Vampire Woman is found only in the moving pictures. You see her in all the new plays and in the magazines, and on the book-covers, and in all the up-to-date advertisements. I read a description of her on the play-bill of a theatre the other day, and it said: "Dowered with a fatal and mesmeric charm, the lure of the iridescent beauty concealed the smallness of the soul within." But that's all right about the soul. I'm not looking for that. I don't care how small it is. Give me the iridescent stuff and I can overlook any shortage of soul that goes with it.

In the magazines the Vampire is generally shown in that scene in her boudoir where her victim (she's been luring him to his destruction) is seen grovelling at her feet. But I never worry about him; he's a nut. Let him grovel.

In the moving pictures you always see the two of them—the Vampire and the Nut—going out together for the evening. He is in evening dress, very pale and with his hair plastered down (poor Nut, he's nearing his end), and she is in her onion-skin dress with a seal cloak thrown over her shoulders. In this dress you see them entering one of those dreadful places where all the men and women— other Nuts and Vampires—are sitting at little tables drinking black sarsaparilla out of champagne glasses, and eating black oysters on the half-shell. In words, the place is one of those that are called "fashionable Hadeses," or words to that effect.

I know those places ever so well by sight—little marble tables and beautiful rubber trees, and Vampires everywhere. I know them. But I can't find them. I wish some one would open up a few fashionable Hadeses in my home town. I know a lot of men who'd go.

Well, that's where the pictured Vampire is principally seen, leading the Nut after her; and, of course, as soon as they sit down at the marble table and she picks up the bill of fare, you *know* that she's going to order a champagne glass of black sarsaparilla and a plate of black oysters. That's all right. Let her. I'd pay for them myself. If I could meet that woman I'd buy her black oysters all the evening.

Later on, you see her dropping little drops of something into the Nut's glass. She's drugging him. I think she puts in little drops of Scotch whisky, or some dreadful stuff like that. In fact, this Vampire Woman doesn't care for the eighteenth amendment one little bit, nor for the interstate commerce clause, nor the Ten Commandments, nor anything. So she drugs the Nut without compunction. And when she has him just about drugged she winds her long arms about his neck, and that is the end of him. At the same time, if she wants *more* men to drug I'll find her a dozen; friends of mine; I know lots of them.

But somehow, wherever you see the pictured Vampire Woman, it's always this lucky Nut who is with her. Sometimes you see them in a motor (they use one about as big as a freight car); sometimes you see them at a Swiss hotel (that's where she throws the Nut over a precipice); and sometimes on an ocean steamer, where there are three thugs, in league with the Vampire, hidden behind a ventilator. But it is always this same kind of Nut that is with her. I wonder at it. It seems as if our whole art and literature—drama, films, magazines, and all—were getting filled up and preoccupied with Vampires and Nuts.

But what I think particularly exasperating is the impossibility of finding the Vamp in real life. Often you think you are very near to it, but you never are. In my own town, for example, there are getting to be a lot of women who look a good bit like Vampires. It's something, I suppose, in the way they dress; not that I ever observe dress at all; like all men, I hardly see it. But I'm wonderfully quick in the absence of it. And very often when I come into the After-Dinner Alley of an hotel, or the corridor of the theatre, I say to myself, " Here are Vampires ! " But they never are. You think they are till you get near them and meet them, and then you're disappointed. The other night, just when I thought I had met a real one, she turned to me and said, " I want so much to introduce my husband." It jarred upon me. And a few nights before that I met two, or what I thought to be two, who had on Onion Skins, and were just going out for the evening. So I took it for granted that they must be going to one of those fashionable Hadeses with the sarsaparilla and the black oysters. I went with them. But it turned out to be a lecture on Recent Advances in Physical Science. Too bad, wasn't it ? Personally, I don't care whether Physical Science advances or goes backward. Especially after that.

I suppose the trouble is that they want to be Vampires and can't. We're such a hopelessly moral race, after two thousand years of law courts and penitentiaries, that we can't be bad if we try to. It's no use. We give a " New Year's Revel," and you couldn't distinguish it in tone from a Sunday-school picnic. We hold a Mardi Gras, and it's as moral as a Mothers' Convention. So I see now why those women went to the Advances in Physical Science. It's the only thing that dares to make them.

And I think I begin to see, too, more in that Nut than I did at first. After all, he has his points about him. Did you notice, in the movies, the reckless way in which he left that pocketbook full of money on the leather seat ? I wouldn't do that.

174

And did you observe how he gave the twenty-dollar gold piece to the doorkeeper; and the way in which, on the steamer, even after they had him drugged, he tried to fight the three thugs all at once ? That little Nut has a size to him that you and I haven't got. And he and the Vampires are primitive elemental types, and we aren't and haven't been for two thousand years. But there's a faint survival in us of what we were that makes us admire them.

In anything that I have said I shouldn't wish to disparage for a moment the splendid types of women that we see about us. It is fine to think of the progress that women have made in this last generation. Everywhere now we have women who vote. We have even women who are fit to hold office and take a seat upon a board. In fact, I know a lot of them that I would be pleased to put on a board and leave there for years.

Oh, no, I have nothing to say against the New Women's movement. I only mean that when it started I got left behind. I imagine that quite a lot of other men did too.

X—"*The Raft*," * an Interlude

(*The kind of Interlude that is sandwiched in for fifteen minutes between the dances in a Musical Revue.*)

THE curtain rises and the light comes on the stage slowly, gradually revealing a raft in the middle of the sea. The dawn is breaking. The raft has the stub of a mast sticking up on it, and there is a chair on it and a litter of boxes and things.

On the raft is a man. He has on white flannel trousers, and a sky-blue flannel shirt, but no collar and tie. He stands up and looks all around the horizon, his hand shading his eyes. He speaks in a sepulchral voice :

" Lost ! Lost ! Alone on the Caribbean Sea ! " (In a more commonplace voice) " At least I think it's the Caribbean. It looks

---

* It is to be noticed that this piece is all ready to put on the stage. Actors anxious for dramatic rights may apply by telegraph or on foot.

176

Caribbean to me. Lost! And not a woman in sight. . . . I thought that in this kind of thing there is always a woman. Ha! Wait! There's one!"

He is much excited and gets a long spy-glass and shoots it in and out at different lengths, searching the sea.

"No!—it's only seaweed. . . . Ba!"

He goes and sits down on a chair and yawns.

"I call this kind of thing dull! There's really nothing to do."

He gets a box of shoe polish and starts to polish his shoes with a rag. Presently—

"I think I'll look around for a woman again. It really is the only thing to do, on a raft—or anywhere else."

He takes his spy-glass and looks again.

"By Jove! Yes! Yes! There's one floating in the sea right there! Quick! Quick!"

In great excitement he runs over to the mast where a little looking-glass hangs, and starts putting on a collar and tie, and brushing his hair in terrible haste. . . . He can't find his collar-stud, etc. etc., and muttering :

> " I must keep calm . . . a woman's life depends on my getting this collar on."

He looks over his shoulder.

> " She's floating nearer."

In the light of the rising sun the girl is now seen floating nearer and nearer.

> " —And nearer—and she's a peach. . . . I *must* save her !   I must plunge in after her."

He stands in the attitude of a person about to dive into the sea, swinging his arms and counting.

> " One—two—*three* . . ." (nearly dives, but checks himself and goes on) " four—five— Six. . . . Ah, I forgot ! I've no swimming costume. . . . Wait a bit, though ! "

He picks up off the raft a long, long pole with a hook on the end.

> " Ha ! "

The girl is quite near now.   He hooks her on the pole and hauls her on to the raft. . . . She sinks down flat on it, inanimate, her eyes closed, her face to the audience. (*Note.*—The girl, of course, is not wet : that would only mess the Act up.)

"What next ?   Ah, one moment."

He runs over to a little bookshelf that is stuck up on the top of the mast, takes out a book, sits down in a chair, and reads aloud very deliberately :

"Rules   for   re — for,   re — sus — for   re-suscitating   the   Damned—the   Drowned : ' In resuscitating the drowned it must be remembered that not a moment must be lost.' "

He settles himself more comfortably in his chair to get a better light to read by.

" ' Every   minute   is   of   vital—of   vital ' —— Humph, I must get my eye-glass."

He goes and hunts it up, polishes it, and continues :

" ' Of vital importance.   First, it is necessary to ascertain whether the heart is still beating.'— Ah ! "

He gets off his chair and on to the floor of the raft on his toes and hands, makes the motions of attempting to put his ear close down on the girl's heart, but keeps withdrawing it with sudden shyness.

"Stop a bit."

He goes and gets a cardboard box and takes out a stethoscope so long that, still standing up, he fixes it to his ears and it reaches the girl's body. He listens and counts, his head on one side and with an air of great absorption.

"One."

A long pause.

"One and a half."

Another pause.

"One—eighty-five—right! She's alive!"

He gets his book again and reads :

"'The strength of the circulation being different in the male and the female sex, the first thing to do if the victim is a woman is to rub her'—to rub her . . ."

He finds it difficult to read, and says conclusively :

"The first thing to do is to rub her. Oh yes ; I see. Now, where shall I begin ? I'll rub her hands."

He takes one of her hands and strokes it very slowly in long, loving strokes. After a moment he plucks at the lace cuff at her wrist.

"Ah, a laundry mark! her name! I must read. Her life hangs on it. 'Edith Croydon!' What a beautiful name!"

He goes on stroking her hand.

  "It doesn't seem to revive her. Oh, very well, there's nothing for it."

He stands up with an air of great determination, and rolls back his cuffs.

  "I must rub her legs."

The girl starts up.

  "Don't you dare! You're no gentleman!"
  "Miss Croydon, you misunderstand my motives!"

He walks away in a huff to the extreme end of the raft and stands with his back turned. The girl meantime runs to the mirror and starts doing her hair, etc.

  "And for the matter of that, I *am* a gentleman. You'll find my card hanging there beside the mirror."

The girl picks down a large card that hangs beside the mirror, and reads :

"HAROLD BORUS,

STORY TALE ADVENTURER

Rafts, Rescues, and other Specialities.
Hairbreadth Escapes Shaved to Order."

  "Oh, Mr. Borus, I'm so sorry! Of course I know all about you—everybody does! I must apologize. Do come back on this part of the raft. Forgive me ! "

Borus, coming back, and taking her hand (with emotion) :

"Miss Croydon, there is nothing to forgive. If I have saved your life, forget it. Let us never speak of it. Think of me not as a hero, but only as a man ! "

"I will."

"And meantime, please make yourself comfortable. Do take this chair. The entire raft, I need hardly say, is at your disposition. You'll find the view from the east side most interesting."

"Thank you so much."

They make themselves comfortable and intimate, she on the chair, he on the soap-box, with elaborate gestures of politeness.

"And do tell me, Mr. Borus, how did you get here ? "

"Very gladly. You won't mind if I begin at the beginning ? "

"Must you ? "

"It's usual . . ."

"Oh, all right."

"Well then " — striking an attitude of recitation—" little did I think——"

" No, I suppose not."

" When I left Havana in a packet——"

" Oh, Mr. Borus, who put you in a packet ? "

" In a packet-boat, that I should be wrecked on the dry Tortugas."

The girl, clasping her hands with agitation :

" The *Dry* Tortugas ! ! Oh, Mr. Borus, have the Tortugas gone dry ? "

" We had hardly left when a great storm arose. . . . A monstrous wave carried away the bridge."

" Good heavens ! "

" We struggled on. A second wave carried away the rudder, the propeller, the wireless apparatus, and the stethoscope ! ! "

" Great heavens ! "

" We struggled on. A third wave carried away the bar. It was at once decided to abandon the ship and lower the boats."

The girl, perplexed :

" But why ? "

" To look for the bar. . . . In the confusion I was left behind. The storm subsided. I continued to make a raft out of a few loose iron beams fastened together by nuts."

" Fastened by nuts, Mr. Borus ? but I thought you were the only one left in the ship ? "

" By nuts. This raft, Miss Croydon, cannot sink ; it is all made of iron."

" How splendid ! And now let me tell you my adventures."

" No, no ; don't trouble, please. You're exhausted ! Don't, you might faint ! "

" Looking back " (the girl goes on very dramatically), " it all seems a blank."

Borus, very hurriedly :

" All right, it's a blank. It's a blank. Let it go at that."

" Mr. Borus, I think you're terribly rude. You might let *me* tell *my* adventures ! "

" Miss Croydon " (very seriously), " how many heroes are there in any story of adventure ? "

" Only one."

" Well, I'm *it*. You must be something else."

Miss Croydon, pettishly :

" I don't want to be. All I know is that I'm cold and I'm hungry, and I don't think that I'll stay ! "

Borus :

"Cold ! Hungry ! ! "

He gets up and starts running round with animation, making preparations.

"Cold ! Ha ha ! I'll soon have a fire for you ! "

"A fire, Mr. Borus, how can you possibly start a fire ? "

Borus laughs.

"A very simple matter, Miss Croydon, to a trained hero like myself."

He has picked up an empty pan and set it on a box.

"I do it simply with sticks rubbed together."

"By rubbing dry sticks together ? Like the Indians I've read about ? How wonderful you are ! "

"I am."

He picks up two or three very little dry twigs.

"I take the dry sticks, *so*——"
"Yes ! Yes ! "
"And first rub them together, *so*——"
"Yes ! Yes ! "
"With a sort of twisting motion."
"Yes ! Yes ! "

"Then I put them in the pan with a bit of paper, *so*" (he takes out a match-box as he speaks) ; "and strike a match and light them."

He lights the paper and the twigs, and they blaze up in a little flame. Edith Croydon and Borus warm their hands at it. She speaks :

"How really wonderful ! "

"Yes. It's the Peruvian method ! And now for food and drink."

The little fire presently flickers out, and has nothing more to do with the Act.

"Have you food and drink on the raft, Mr. Borus ? I think you are simply superb."

"I am. Now let me see." (He starts taking things out of a box.) "What have we here ? Tinned *pâté de foie gras*."

"Lovely ! "

"Canned asparagus. Do you like canned asparagus ? "

"Oh, I worship it ! "

"Tin of boneless pheasant."

"Oh, Mr. Borus, I'm just mad over boneless pheasant ! "

Borus, taking out the cans and reading the labels (with exclamations from the girl) :

"Boneless pheasant—finless fish—spineless

sardines—tongueless tongue . . . now what shall it be first ? "

Borus with great *empressement* has just laid a little white cloth on a soap-box, and quickly spread out glasses and dishes and knives and forks till it has the appearance of an appetizing preparation. They both accompany it with exclamations of interest and delight. Miss Croydon says :

> " Let me see. I think I'd like, first, *pâté de foie gras* and finless fish, and just a teeny bit of shell-less lobster, and—and——"

When suddenly Borus has sprung to his feet with a sort of howl.

> " Oh, Mr. Borus, what is it ? "

Borus, casting his hands to heaven :

> " I haven't got—I haven't got——"
> " Yes—yes——"
> " I forgot——"
> " Yes—yes—you forgot——"
> " The can-opener ! Great heavens, we have no can-opener ! ! "

The girl exclaims :

> " No can-opener ! " (and falls forward on the table).

Borus :

"Stop ! Wake up ! I can open them ! "

He makes a wild attack on the tins, beating the
and stamping on them, and biting them, etc. e
Presently he subsides in despair and collapses on t
soap-box.

"It's no good, Miss Croydon. We mu
eat the tins. You eat first. You are a woman
"No, Mr. Borus, not yet. We can
least "—she speaks with tragedy — "dri
Let us drink before we die."

Borus :

"You are right. We can drink before
die. It is more than a lot of people can do."

He recovers something of his animation and beg
taking out bottles and setting them on the table.

"There ! Bottled ale. Bass's bottled ale
"Oh, Mr. Borus, how divine ! I j
worship Bass's bottled ale."
"Now, then, get your glass ready."
"Right."

Then he leaps up again with a howl.

"What is it, Mr. Borus—oh, what is it ? "

"The thing—the thing you open it with ! !
I haven't got one ! "

They both collapse. Borus slightly recovering,
but gloomily :

"There's a way of opening these bottles
with a fifty-cent piece . . ."

Miss Croydon, brightly :

"Oh, never mind, I think I have a dollar
bill in my purse."

Business here of trying to open the bottle by holding
a dollar bill over it. At last Borus says :

"It's no good, Miss Croydon. We must
resign ourselves to our fate. If we must
die "—he takes a noble attitude—" you are
a woman. Die first ! "

There is a sadness, and then Miss Croydon says :

" Mr. Borus, it's getting dark."

Borus looks up at the sky.

"Yes, the sun will soon set."
"Already, Mr. Borus ? "
"Yes, Miss Croydon. Night comes quickly
in the tropics. Look, the sun is setting."

The sun, seen as a round, red disk at the back of
the stage, begins to set in jumps, about a yard at a

time. When it has got near the bottom it takes a long whirl up again and then goes under. The stage is half dark.

Borus :

"It is night ! "

"Night ? Here on the raft ? Oh, I mustn't stay ! "

"Miss Croydon, I intend to treat you with the chivalry of a hero. One moment."

Borus takes an oar and sticks it up, and takes a big, grey blanket and fastens it across the raft like a partition, so as to divide the raft in two.

"Miss Croydon " (says Borus, looking over the top of the blanket), "that end of the raft is absolutely *yours*."

"How chivalrous you are ! "

"Not at all. I shall not intrude upon you in any way. Good night."

"Good night, Mr. Borus."

They each begin making preparations for sleep, one each side of the curtain. Borus stands up and puts his head over again.

"You'll find a candle and matches near your bed."

"Oh, thank you, Mr. Borus; how noble you are!"

"Not at all."

After another little interlude Borus puts his head over the top again.

"I am now putting my head over this blanket for the last time. If there is anything you want, say so now. And remember if you want anything in the night do not hesitate to call me. I shall be here—at any moment. I promise it. Good night."

"Good night, Mr. Borus."

They settle down in the growing darkness for a few minutes as if falling asleep.

Then all of a sudden a bright light, a searchlight, comes shining over the sea, full on the raft. They both start up.

"Oh, Mr. Borus, look, look! A light—a ship!!"

Borus :

"A light—a ship! They may have a cork-screw! We're saved. Look—it's a large yacht—a pleasure yacht."

There are voices heard.

"Raft, ahoy!" (and shouts).

Miss Croydon :

"A pleasure yacht! Oh, then I recognize it!"

"You recognize it?"

"It's the yacht I fell out of this morning."

"Fell out of——"

"Yes. You wouldn't let me tell you . . ."

There is a call across the water :

"Raft ahoy! Stand by! We're lowering a boat."

Borus :

"Saved! Saved! But there is just one thing I want to say before we go aboard. . . . Miss Croydon—Edith—since I've been on this raft I've learned to love you as I never could have anywhere else. Edith, will you be my wife?"

Miss Croydon, falling into his arms :

"Will I? Oh, Harold, that's what I fell out of the yacht for!"

CURTAIN.

OTHER FANCIES

XI—First Call for Spring; or, Oh, Listen to the Birds!

I GATHER that spring is approaching. I am not an observant man, but, as the days go by, the signs begin to multiply, even for me, that mean that spring is at hand.

I take this early occasion to notify the public of my opinion and to support it with collateral facts. I am anxious this year to be among the first in the field. Among the signs on which I base my view that spring is near, I may mention that I observe that the snow has gone; that the Income-tax declarations are being distributed at the post office; and that the sign " Bock Beer " is hung out at the Marshal Foch Café, formerly the Kaiserhof. (American papers, please suppress sign No. 3 for fear of public riots.)

Spring, then, is upon us. The first call for spring has come: and I should like to suggest that this year we meet it firmly and quietly and with none of the hysterical outburst that it usually provokes in people of a certain temperament. I refer to those unfortunate beings called " lovers of Nature."

Each year I have been pained to notice that the approach of spring occasions a most distressing aberration in the conduct of many of my friends. Beside my house, a few doors on the right, I have an acquaintance who is a Nature Man. All through the winter he is fairly quiet, and an agreeable friendly fellow, quite fit for general society. I notice him, it is true, occasionally grubbing under the snow. I have once or twice seen him break off a frozen twig from a tree, and examine it. On one occasion, indeed, last winter, he was temporarily unmanned by seeing a black bird (otherwise harmless) sitting on a bough. But for the most part his conduct during the colder weather is entirely normal.

Spring, however, at once occasions in my Nature friend a distressing disturbance. He seems suddenly to desire, at our every meeting, to make himself a channel of information as between the animate world and me. From the moment that the snow begins to melt, he keeps me posted as to what the plants and the birds and the bees are doing. This is a class of information which I do not want, and which I cannot use. But I have to bear it.

My Nature friend passes me every morning with some new and bright piece of information— something that he thinks so cheery that it irradiates

his face. " I saw a finch this morning," he says.
" Oh, did you," I answer. " I noticed a scarlet
tanager this afternoon," says my friend. " You
don't say so ! " I reply. What a tanager is I have
never known : I hope I never shall. When my
Nature friend says things of this sort, all I can do
is to acquiesce. I can't match his information in
any way. In point of ornithology I only know
two birds, the crow and the hen. I can tell them
at once either by their plumage or by their song.
I can carry on a Nature conversation up to the
limit of the crow and the hen ; beyond that,
not.

So, for the first day or so in spring, I am able to
say, " I saw a crow yesterday," or " I noticed a
hen out walking this morning." But somehow
my crow and hen seem to get out of date awfully
quickly. I get ashamed of them and never refer
to them again. But my friend keeps up his information for weeks, running through a whole
gamut of animals. " I saw a gopher the other
day," he says, " guess what the little fellow was
doing ? " If only he knew it, I'd like to break out
and answer, " I don't care what the Hades the
little fellow was doing." But, like everybody else,
I suppose, I have not the assurance or the cruelty
to break in upon the rapture of the Nature Man.
Some day I shall ; and when I do let him watch out.

My particular anger with these Nature Men, such as my friend, springs, I think, from the singularly irritating kind of language that they use : a sort of ingratiating wee-wee way in which they amalgamate themselves, as it were, with Nature. They really seem to feel so cute about it. If a wee hepatica peeps above the snow, they think they've done it. They describe it to you in a peculiar line of talk almost like baby language. " What do you think I saw ? " says the Nature Man. " Just the tiniest little shoot of green peeping from the red-brown of the willow ! " He imitates it with his thumb and finger to show the way the tiny little shoot shoots. I suppose he thinks he's a little bud himself. I really believe that my particular friend actually imagines himself in spring-time to be a wee hepatica, or a first crocus, or the yellow under-leaf of a daffodil.

And notice, too, the way in which they refer to colours : never plain and simple ones like red or black or blue ; always stuff like " red-brown " or " blue-green." My friend asks me if I have noticed the peculiar soft " yellow-brown " that the water-fowl puts on in spring. Answer : No, I haven't. I haven't seen any water-fowl ; I don't know where you look for them, and I didn't know that they put anything on. As for " yellow-brown," I didn't know that there was any such colour. I have seen a blue-black crow this year, and I have noticed a burnt-indigo-sepia hen ; but beyond that I have not seen anything doing.

Worst of all, and, in fact, verging on paresis, is the state of mind of the Nature Man in regard to the birds. When he speaks of them, his voice takes on a peculiar whine. My Nature friend told me yesterday that he had seen two orioles just beginning to build a nest behind his garage. He said he " tiptoed " to the spot (notice the peculiar wee-wee language that these people use) and then stood rooted there watching them. I forget whether he said " rooted " or " riveted " : on occasions like this he sometimes reports himself as one and sometimes as the other. But why on earth, if he is once fairly rooted, does he come unrooted again ?

I therefore wish to give this plain and simple notice, meant without malice : If any other of my friends has noticed a snowdrop just peeping above the edge of the turf, will he mind not telling me ? If one of them has noticed that the inner bark of the oak is beginning to blush a faint blue-red, would he mind keeping it to himself ? If there is any man that I know who has seen two orioles starting to build a nest behind his garage, and if he has stood rooted to the ground with interest, and watched the dear little feathered pair fluttering to and fro, would he object to staying rooted and saying nothing about it ?

I am aware that I ought long ago to have spoken out openly to my Nature friends. But I have, I admit, the unfortunate and weak-minded disposition that forces me to smile with hatred in my heart. My unhappy neighbour does not suspect that I mean to kill him. But I do. I have stood for all that tanager and oriole stuff that I can. The end is coming. And as for that hepatica just putting its tiny face above the brown of the leaf— well, wait, that's all. Some day, I know it, I shall all of a sudden draw a revolver on my friend and say, " Listen. This has gone far enough. Every spring for many years you have stopped me in the street and told me of this Nature stuff. And I have stood for it and smiled. You told me when the first touch of brown appeared on the underwing of the lark, and I let you say it. You kept me posted as to when the first trillium appeared from a pile of dead oak leaves under a brush-heap ; and I let you tell it to me and never said that all I knew of trilliums was in connection with the German reparations indemnity. But the thing is exhausted. Meet your fate as you can. You are going where the first purple-pink of the young rhododendron will be of no interest to you."

I don't want to appear surly. But I am free to

admit that I am the kind of man who would never notice an oriole building a nest unless it came and built it in my hat in the hat-room of the club. There are other men like me too; and the time has come when we must protect ourselves. There are signs of spring that every sensible man respects and recognizes. He sees the oysters disappear from the club bill-of-fare, and knows that winter is passing; he watches boiled new California potatoes fall from 25 to 10 cents a portion, and realizes that the season is advancing. He noted the first timid appearance of the asparagus just peeping out of its melted butter; and he sees the first soft blush on the edge of the Carolina strawberry at one dollar and fifty cents a box. And he watches, or he used to watch, in the old days beyond recall, for the sign " BOCK BEER TO-DAY " that told him that all Nature was glad.

These are the signs of spring that any man can appreciate. They speak for themselves. Viewed thus, I am as sensitive to the first call for spring as any of my fellows. I like to sit in my club with my fellow-members of like mind and watch its coming and herald its approach.

But for the kind of spring that needs a whole text-book of biology to interpret it, I have neither use nor sympathy.

XII—How I succeeded in my Business

(Secrets of Success as revealed by the Best Current Literature)

I HAD been employed in one business and another quite a good few years, more years than I cared to look back upon ; and yet I hadn't made good. I hadn't made good, and I knew I hadn't made good, and sometimes the knowledge that I hadn't made good made me feel bad. Often I said to my wife when I came home at nights, " Doll," I said, " I haven't made good." " No, Jim, old boy," she'd say, " I know you haven't made good, but never mind, you'll make good yet." And then I'd see a tear fall from her eye on to the dresser. After that I'd go out and sit in the back-yard and feel real bad.

Often I used to think it over as to why it was I hadn't made good. I'd had about as much educa-tion as most, and more experience than many, and better chances than some. I was willing enough and steady enough. I was a non-drinker and a non-smoker ; I never touched a card and had never seen a horse-race in my life, and never been inside the doors of a pool-room. Yet I knew as well as anybody just where my shortcomings were : I lacked pep, I had no punch, I had practically no magnetism, and I didn't react quickly on a given environment. And I knew that nowadays in business it is magnetism, and pep, and reaction that make for success. Then, too, I failed in the little things : I couldn't add up more than one column of figures at a time, and my memory was no good ; things seemed to slip out of it. Often when I came home of an evening I'd say to my wife, " Doll," I'd say, " my memory is no good." " What is it you can't remember, Jim ? " she'd say. " I forget," I'd answer ; and I'd groan.

Then, also, though of course I didn't know it, my diet was all wrong. Every morning I filled myself up with coffee, and I was a meat-eater, and I used to enjoy every meal I ate without any idea of the proper proportion of farraginous and nitrogenous units. I had no notion in those days that for every unit of albuminous farrago that a man eats he ought to have a definite quantity of hydrogen and a fixed proportion of pollen.

Well, I was thinking it all over one Monday morning in the backyard before going to work, when all of a sudden the reason of my failure came to me like a flash. I had no belief in myself : that was it. I couldn't accomplish anything because I couldn't believe in myself and didn't react upon myself. I got up and I walked right into the house, to the kitchen where Doll was getting the breakfast ready. " Doll," I said, " I've found out what was wrong. I've got to believe in myself," and I hit the table with my fist till it jumped up. " Oh, Jim," Doll said, " you frighten me ! " " Ha ha ! " I laughed—that was the first time in six years Doll had ever said that I frightened her—" I frighten you, do I ? Well, then, fetch me some farraginous food." " Won't you have your bacon ? " says Doll. " I was just getting it ready." " No, Doll," I said, " don't you realize that bacon contains more units of nitrogen than I can absorb in the office ? The attempt to absorb nitrogenous food, Doll, depresses the nerve centres and lowers the tone of the system. Get me some sour buttermilk and half a dipper of baked beans, so cooked as to emphasize their albuminous properties." " Coffee ? " said Doll. " No, Doll," I answered, " not a drop. Get me a little popped bran, mixed with warm water."

Well, I got my breakfast and I started down to the office for my new job, just feeling fine. I could sense myself reacting against everything. " Jim Dudley," I kept repeating to myself, " you're going to make good."

The first person I ran into at the office was the general manager, just going in.

" You're ten minutes early, Dudley," he said.

" Mr. Kitson," I answered, " I'd rather be early than not : the employé who values his employer's time more than his own reacts backward to his own emolument."

And with that I opened my desk and got right to work. I guess I never worked in my life as I did that morning. Everything seemed easy. Letters I would have taken half an hour to consider I answered in two minutes. And every letter I answered I tried to put in just a little sunshine. Even if I didn't know who the correspondent was, I found time to write in " Peek-a-boo ! " or " Keep on smiling ! " or some little thing like that. " Jim Dudley," I said to myself, " you're going to make good."

Two or three times in the morning Mr. Kitson walked through the office. " Hard at it, Dudley," he said.

" Mr. Kitson," I answered, " the employé who is not hard at it is defrauding both himself and his employer of his proper integument."

Well, along about one o'clock Mr. Kitson came over to my desk. " Dudley," he said, " I've something I want to talk to you about. Come out to have lunch with me."

"All right, Mr. Kitson," I answered. "I've one more post card to write, and then I'll come."

"Never mind the post card, Jim," he said, "that can look after itself."

"Mr. Kitson," I said, "Napoleon used to make it a rule never to begin a post card without finishing it."

Well, I got the post card all nicely fixed up and signed, and got my hat and went out with Mr. Kitson to a swell club. There was a big bill of fare, but I took no meat at all, only half a bucket of spinach. I noticed that Mr. Kitson ate nothing but boiled water-cress.

"Now, Jim," said Mr. Kitson, "I've had my eye on you all the morning, and I believe you're the man we want. The company wants some one to go to Kansas City to line up a man and to swing a big proposition."

"Mr. Kitson," I interrupted, "I can line him up and swing it."

"When can you go?"

"Right now," I said, "as soon as I finish my spinach. Just tell me what it is that I swing when I get there."

"Good!" he said. "The man that you are to see is John Smith of John Street. Can you remember the name? Better write it down."

"I don't need to," I said. "Just say the name

over three or four times and my memory will take a grip on it. I'll take a few deep breaths while you say it."

So I went right over to the house and packed my grip.

"Doll," I said, "I'm off to Kansas City."

"What to do?" Doll asked.

"To swing a proposition," I answered. "It's a big thing, Doll, with big people, and if I make good we'll come out big."

I left on the cars that night, and all the way out I ate grass and cultivated my memory and reacted all the time on everything I saw.

Well, when I got to Kansas City, I found I was up against something pretty big, all right. I found John Smith, but he wouldn't see me. I went right into his office, and I said, "Mr. Smith, can I see you?" "No," he said, "you can't." However, I hung on. "Let me see you," I said. "No, I won't," he answered. Still I wouldn't give in. I went up to his house that evening and right into his library. "Can I see you now?" I asked. "No," he answered, "you can't see me." "Look here, Mr. Smith," I pleaded; "I've come two thousand miles to see you; let me see you!" "No, Dudley," he said, "I won't."

That went on four days, and at last he gave in. "All right, Jim," he said, "state your business.

What do you want ? " " I want to line you up—
swing you," I said. " Come out with me, Mr.
Smith, and eat spinach, and I'll tell you about
it."

So I took him out to a swell restaurant where
they had the best spinach in Kansas City. " Now,"
I said, after we had eaten, " you're a big man and
this is a big thing : we want to put over something
pretty big, and you're the man we want in on it.
You're big."

" Jim," he said, " you talk well. And, what's
more, you've got personality, and that's the biggest
thing in business to-day. As soon as I see a man
who has personality, I do whatever he wants. Personality gets me every time."

So I got what I wanted, and I took the train
right back to New York. Doll met me at the depot.
I kissed her right there on the platform. " Did
you swing it ? " she asked. " Yes, Doll, I did," I
answered. I saw Doll drop a tear right on the
platform. " Good old Jim," she said.

Next morning I found an envelope on my desk
with a cheque for five thousand dollars in it.

Well, that was how I got my first start. Once
the firm found that I could line up a man and
swing a thing of that size, there was lots more for
me to do. So the end of it was they made me the
head of the company. " It's no use trying to keep

you down, Jim," said Mr. Kitson. "You're the biggest of all of us."

So I went home to Doll and I said, "Doll," I said, "I'm made president of the company."

"Oh, Jim!" she said, "you've made good. I'm so proud—and I'm proud of the company, too, now that you're president of it. So you must tell me all about it, what it does and what it makes and sells."

"Doll," I answered, "don't ask me. I've been so busy swinging propositions and lining things up and breathing and eating spinach, that I've never had time to find out what on earth the company does do."

XIII—The Dry Banquet

I HAD once a good friend, now gone from this scene, whose custom it was, on any and each occasion when a topic of importance came up, to say, "Well, let us start a national movement about it."

As I remember it, he never got far with any of them. He generally started them at our club at lunch, which is always the brightest hour of the social reformer. "Let us organize ourselves into an informal committee," he would say. And he organized us. It was done, as I recall it, merely by pushing the bell and ordering another bottle of claret.

But after lunch my friend always fell asleep, and somehow, by the time he woke, the national movement had vanished. He is gone now where there are no national movements and no organization. But I have served, I hope with distinction, on so great a number of his informal committees that something of the habit clings to me.

I have a national movement that I want to

organize now. And I know no better way of doing it than through the pages of this book. I want to gather together into one single compact body all my fellow-sufferers of the dry banquet, and, when I have us together, I want to hurl us with irresistible impact at the walls of society. Of our power there can be no doubt. I believe that if we were extended in a single line we would reach nearly to Havana. Unfortunately, not quite.

But observe that I am not saying a word, here and now, against Prohibition. I am only talking of the obvious insanity, under Prohibition, of keeping up the peculiar institution called a BANQUET. Even the most ardent Prohibitionist will admit that the original meaning of a Banquet was a gathering for the sake of eating and drinking. It may have been wrong. But that was the idea. And what is more, they didn't drink water.

At Belshazzar's Feast, when Belshazzar arose and said, " Gentlemen, I want you to rise and fill your glasses, and drink to the health of a man whom this city of Babylon delights to honour, a man whom we have the privilege of entertaining to-night, Mr. Nebuchadnezzar "—when he said that, the Babylonians did not fill up their glasses with water, or lift up their coffee cups and make a pretence of drinking from the gold dregs of a *demitasse*.

If you remove the drinking of toasts from a banquet, you are acting the play of *Hamlet* without Hamlet. For the eating part of it is at best only Ophelia.

If there is anything more conspicuously silly than a group of two or three hundred men being invited to " fill up their glasses " and drink pint after pint of water to the health of their fellow-sufferer, I want to see it. If you add to this the fact that heavy eating has already brought them to the verge of somnolence, that their native spirits are buried under four pounds of beefsteak, some idea may be formed of the ironic misery of a dry " banquet."

Speaking in a personal sense, I do not want to seem ungrateful for the hospitality I have received. But I have attended four dry banquets in the last four weeks, and am suffering still. At the latest of them I drank a pint of water to the health of the President of the United States. I drank, as a loyal British subject, nearly a quart for King George. I drank half a pint to the Supreme Court of the United States ; one pint to our Great Universities ; two each to our larger railroads ; and one gill to the League of Nations. It is, speaking frankly, just a little too much.

Even more dreadful to contemplate is the awful quantity of food devoured, in sheer ennui, at the dry banquet. With the absence of wine, the lightness of the thing is lost. There is nothing to do but eat. I have seen a man sit and eat celery, at the opening of a dry banquet, for twenty minutes from sheer misery of soul. I have watched another eat forty-two olives one after the other. I have even noticed men pick the table decorations off the cloth and eat them ; and last week I saw a man eat a flag without observing what it was. When the different meats are brought, the guests go on eating automatically and undiscerningly ; they only stop when there is no more.

Last month at one single sitting we each ate :

> 10 olives.
> 2 yards of celery.
> 1 half-bucket of soup.
> 12 sq. inches filet de sole Momay.
> 16 oz. avoirdup. Virginia ham.
> 16   „   beef au J.
> 108 cubic centimetres soufflé.

And after that we lost track, and sat among a welter of French pastry, cheese, and fruit, scarcely conscious. And right at the end I saw my left-hand neighbour reach out and eat a radish. Some of us would have eaten nuts, but we had no strength to crack them.

And then, it is at this moment of the dry banquet

that the toastmaster, merry fellow, rises with his glass of water and starts up the oratory of the evening.

In the wicked old days, now amended constitutionally, the speeches were supposed to be gay. Laughter was the order of the evening. I am quite sure that, at Belshazzar's Feast, Mr. Nebuchadnezzar had no sooner got upon his feet than the whole room was filled with a pleasant expectancy. "Well, gentlemen," he would say, "I want to tell you that I am glad to be here!" That was all that was needed. The company burst into a roar of merriment. There was, or was supposed to be, something so droll in the way in which Mr. Nebuchadnezzar got up, something so inimitable in the way in which he looked about him round the room, that the impulse to laughter was irresistible. And when Mr. Nebuchadnezzar went on to say, "I want to tell you, gentlemen, a little story about a commercial traveller who was going from Babylon to Damascus," the room became a mere uproar of laughter and applause.

But now! *O tempora, O mores!* The after-dinner speeches have changed into after-dinner lectures. Nebuchadnezzar rises in his place, serious, lantern-jawed, and dull. Who ever could have thought the fellow amusing! He faces an audience, heavy, somnolent, bored to death already, hating everything and everybody, and only wanting to be gone.

Then he makes a speech on the Babylonian Canal System. There are reporters sitting all around him writing it down on tablets of mud. He gives all the statistics of the mileage of the Babylonian canals, he goes into the technique of the siltage of the mud, he touches lightly on the new mud-shovel, he assures the auditors that we can now lift fifty tons of mud per hour. You can almost feel him lifting it as he talks. And the next day the Babylonian papers record the gay gathering with a great capital heading — " FIFTY TONS OF MUD PER HOUR—Enjoyable Gathering at the Belshazzar Banquet."

This is what is going on about us every evening. And for some reason or other there has arisen a sort of conspiracy of silence in regard to it. There is such a decent tradition abroad among us about the acceptance of hospitality that no invited guest cares to refuse his invitation. He accepts. He goes. He stands, mournful and resigned, among the little group of the reception committee waiting for the banquet to begin. He walks like a dumb sheep into the banquet hall to the music of " Hail, Columbia ! " He eats with due submission his four pounds of beefsteak. He endures the full mud-shovel of statistics that is dumped over him ;

and, still suffering, reaches, at last, the happy moment when he may wrap his fur-lined coat about him and step out into the night. Not even the immortal words of Bryant's "Thanatopsis" can present, to our minds, a deeper picture of the welcome of everlasting sleep.

If we must be Prohibitionists, why not do the thing properly? If the wine is out, away with the Banquet. Let us do all things in order. Let us gather without food or drink and bring our knitting and our crochet-work instead. Then, to the cheerful clicking of the busy needles, let us hear with pleased attentiveness the proud statistics of our transportation system.

I have reason to know that there are others, thousands of others, who suffer as I do. Some of them are so highly placed that to mention their names might crack the Constitution. One is an Ambassador, several are Governors of State, many, a great many, are Generals, and one a Prince. I can only hope that when the definite announcement of my New Movement is made they will get their knitting needles together and join in.

In short, the Banquet was, even at its best and in the happy days of cocktails and with the merriment due to the presence of gentlemen charmingly urbane under the influence of stimulants, a terrifying thing at best. It was stilted, formal, opposed to true sociability and cheer. But the magical philtres, the happy draughts of southern wine, made it a thing, not agreeable, but at least tolerable.

But now, without the miraculous potions, without, in short, the means of achieving the warm heart under the white shirt, the thing is a stark and naked horror. Frankly, it makes only for ill-feeling, for the loss of anything like the love we once held for our fellow-men.

XIV—My Lost Dollar

MY friend Todd owes me a dollar. He has owed it to me for twelve months, and I fear there is little prospect of his ever returning it. I can realize whenever I meet him that he has forgotten that he owes me a dollar. He meets me in the same frank, friendly way as always. My dollar has clean gone out of his mind. I see that I shall never get it back.

On the other hand, I know that I shall remember all my life that Todd owes me a dollar. It will make no difference, I trust, to our friendship, but I shall never be able to forget it. I don't know how it is with other people; but if any man borrows a dollar from me I carry the recollection of it to the grave.

Let me relate what happened. Todd borrowed this dollar last year on the 8th of April (I mention the date in case this should ever meet Todd's eye), just as he was about to leave for Bermuda. He needed a dollar in change to pay his taxi; and I lent it to him. It happened quite simply and naturally ; I hardly realized it till it was all over. He merely said, " Let me have a dollar, will you ? " And I said, " Certainly. Is a dollar enough ? " I believe, in fact I *know*, that when Todd took that dollar he meant to pay for it.

He sent me a note from Hamilton, Bermuda. I thought when I opened it that the dollar would be in it. But it wasn't. He merely said that the temperature was up to nearly 100. The figure misled me for a moment.

Todd came back in three weeks. I met him at the train—not because of the dollar, but because I really esteem him. I felt it would be nice for him to see some one waiting for him on the platform after being away for three weeks. I said, " Let's take a taxi up to the Club." But he answered, " No, let's walk."

We spent the evening together, talking about Bermuda. I was thinking of the dollar, but of course I didn't refer to it. One simply can't. I asked him what currency is used in Bermuda, and whether the American dollar goes at par (I put a slight emphasis on *the* American dollar), but found again that I could not bring myself to make any reference to it.

It took me some time (I see Todd practically every day at my Club) to realize that he had completely forgotten the dollar. I asked him one day what his trip cost him, and he said that he kept no accounts. A little later I asked him if he felt settled down after his trip, and he said that he had practically forgotten about it. So I knew it was all over.

In all this I bear Todd no grudge. I have simply added him to the list of men who owe me a dollar and who have forgotten it. There are quite a few of them now. I make no difference in my demeanour to them, but I only wish that I could forget.

I meet Todd very frequently. Only two nights ago I met him out at dinner and he was talking, apparently without self-consciousness, about Poland. He said that Poland would never pay her debts. You'd think a thing like that would have reminded him, wouldn't you ? But it didn't seem to.

But meantime a thought—a rather painful thought—has begun to come into my mind at intervals. It is this. If Todd owes me a dollar and has forgotten it, it is possible—indeed it is theoretically probable—that there must be men to whom I owe a dollar which I have forgotten. There may be a list of them. The more I think of it the less I like it, because I am quite sure that if I had once forgotten a dollar I should never pay it, on this side of the grave.

If there *are* such men, I want them to speak out.

Not all at once; but in reasonable numbers, and as far as may be in alphabetical order, and I will immediately write their names down on paper. I don't count here men who may have lent me an odd dollar over a bridge table; and I am not thinking (indeed, I am taking care not to think) of the man who lent me thirty cents to pay for a bottle of plain soda in the Detroit Athletic Club last month. I always find that there's nothing like plain soda after a tiring ride across the Canadian frontier, and that man who advanced that thirty cents knows exactly why I felt that I had done enough for him. But if any man ever lent me a dollar to pay for a taxi when I was starting for Bermuda I want to pay it.

More than that. I want to start a general movement, a *Back to Honesty* movement, for paying all these odd dollars that are borrowed in moments of expansion. Let us remember that the greatest nations were built up on the rock basis of absolute honesty.

In conclusion, may I say that I do particularly ask that no reader of this book will be careless enough to leave this copy round where it might be seen by Major Todd, of the University Club of Montreal?

XV—Radio, a New Form of Trouble

WHAT is Radio ? I shall be only too glad if any reader of this book will write and tell me, simply and in words that I can understand, what Radio is.

Let him understand at the outset that it is no use telling me that by means of Radio, I would be able, seated comfortably in my own arm-chair, to hear the Pittsburg orchestra. I know it. I don't want to. Nor need he inform me that, seated comfortably in my own arm-chair, I can hear a speech by W. J. Bryan. I don't need to. I heard one.

Nor do I wish for information involving the use of such words, " receiving circuit," " rheostat," and " varioeter." These words are no help to me. I have tried them out, and I don't get them. I have already read a little book called *Radio for the Beginner*, and it has beaten me. I have sent away for another that is called *Radio for Infants*, but I have very little hope from it. I know already that it will tell me that any infant nowadays, seated comfortably in his high chair, can hear the Pittsburg orchestra. And of course it will contain what are called " directions " telling me to "insert my antennæ in my ears." But I refuse to. It sounds like insults that we used to use when I was young.

And, most particularly, I don't want surprising statements about the rapidity of ether waves. It is no use telling me that the Hertzian waves represent 3,000,000,000,000,000 oscillations per second. I believe that that figure is correct, but it doesn't strike me as so terribly fast anyway. After reading for months the statistical figures on the Bill of Reparations against Germany and the fall of the Russian Rouble, it leaves me cold.

All that I clearly perceive about Radio is, that a new form of trouble has broken out in the world. One more item has been added to the growing lists of *Things I Don't Understand*. I know now just how they felt in Ancient Babylon when they hanged the man who invented the first wheelbarrow. Radio, in short, just adds one length to the distance which I am being left behind.

Indeed, the whole Radio business, as I read it in the newspapers, seems to be largely in the hands of children. Only last week I noticed that a little boy in the Schenectady Technical High School

had made a Radio machine out of an empty sardine
can and a piece of stove-pipe wire. He must be a
bright little fellow. I'd like to choke him. And I
see where another bright little fellow (they are
called "bright little fellows" in Radio literature)
has fixed up a Radio set in his bedroom : it said
that his "aerial" was 75 feet long and that he had
a "flat top lead-in." Poor boy ! I forget what he
uses his Radio set for. Perhaps he listens to the
Pittsburg orchestra. They mostly do.

Meantime the thing has assumed the proportions
of a vast movement. There are Radio shops, Radio
fans, and a whole growth of Radio literature,
magazines, journals, advertisements, and prize com-
petitions. In fact, it's a "world movement";
it takes its place right alongside of Prohibition and
psycho-analysis and the subconscious mind. In
a very short time it will get into the moving pictures
and on the stage, and into our current novels and
the heart of our literature. I was reading the
other night—or was I dreaming ?—a "Radio
novel," which began something like this :

"Angelina sat in her cloistered room, her antennæ in her ears and her eyes idly resting on her
direction-finder, hearing and yet half not hearing
the Pittsburg orchestra, while the Hertzian waves
moved drowsily past her at the rate of three million
billion miles a second. Suddenly the girl noted

among the waves one which sent a throb to her heart. It was his—Edward's. That familiar and beloved call, ' K double Z, O double Z.' She would recognize it anywhere. There was a romance about it which thrilled the young girl—' K ZZ O ZZ.'

" Hastily she adjusted her amplifier, moved her spark to a better audio-frequency, and opened her condenser tie ; its capacity increased one-millionth of a farad. ' Edward,' she clicked. ' It is I. Where are you ? ' ' I am here,' came the answer, ' seated comfortably in my arm-chair ; I am listening to a broadcast by one of our greatest national preachers. Tune your wave-length, darling ' (he said the word in Radio), ' QQ is the sign for it, " F " and cut in and we will listen to it together.' ' I will, sweetheart,' she answered (HKW).

" Rapidly the bright young girl—she was in the highest grade of the Schenectady Technical High School : the last one that they will allow them to be in—adjusted her Radio set. In a few moments she had cut in on the same broadcast that Edward, far away in the ether, was also absorbing into his vacuum tube. It was wonderful to the girl to think that her antennæ were joined to his by the same wave, and that his amplitude and hers, with a proportional deduction for the square of the distance, were now in the circuit.

"Thus together they listened to the broadcast, their antennæ close locked——"

And would you believe it, by the time I had got to this point in the narration of the new Radio novel, all of a sudden it began; it seemed strangely like, and yet unlike, something that I had read long ago in a forgotten story dealing with New England life in the older days.

Something like this it went: "Together they sat and listened to the voice of the preacher in the pulpit, and as they sat thus, his hand found hers, and their hands remained as they listened, close locked together——"

Queer, isn't it? The similarity. This new world is not quite as might appear. And on the whole I must say I prefer the hand to the antennæ.

Not but what there are great advantages about the new Radio method as thus applied. Before John Strongface (I think that was his name in the New England novel—either that or John Ironheart) could get Priscilla to that pew in the church where he held her hand, he had to walk eight miles through the forest on his snowshoes with bears after him, and after the service was over he had to help her put on her wraps and tie her muffler round her neck, and take her home four miles and eat pumpkin pie with her mother.

Whereas Edward, with his Radio set! a cinch!

No trouble about taking her home, no expense, nothing. All he has to do is to " cut her out." It is done like this :

" Somehow he felt that the vibration of the girl's battery was growing fainter. ' Tired, love,' he whispered (ZZZZ) (a whisper is indicated by four loud blue sparks). ' A little,' she amplified. ' Then let us cut out,' signalled Edward, ' and to-morrow night at eight, seated comfortably in our arm-chairs, we will listen to the Pittsburg orchestra.' ' That will be lovely, dearest,' she answered. (QQQ)——

" Then this pure girl—she was taking pure mathematics and pure physics at the Schenectady Technical High School—clicked out her simple prayers on her Radio, and sank to rest."

There ! Out of all which there seems to grow a moral. I could feel it growing while I was writing this, but it seems to slip away from me at the end. Something about all the rush and bustle of our modern life, full of inventions and machinery and wonders, leaving us no further on after all. Eh, what ?

XVI—Roughing it in the Bush

(My plans for Moose-Hunting in the Canadian Wilderness)

THE season is now opening when all those who have a manly streak in them like to get out into the bush and " rough it " for a week or two of hunting or fishing. For myself, I never feel that the autumn has been well spent unless I can get out after the moose. And, when I go, I like to go right into the bush and " rough it "— get clear away from civilization, out in the open, and take fatigue and hardship just as it comes.

So this year I am making all my plans to get away for a couple of weeks of moose-hunting along with my brother George and my friend Tom Gass. We generally go together because we are all of us men who like the rough stuff, and are tough enough to stand the hardship of living in the open. The place we go to is right in the heart of the primitive Canadian forest, among big timber, broken with lakes as still as glass, just the very ground for moose.

We have a kind of lodge up there. It's just a rough place that we put up, the three of us, the year before last—built out of tamarack logs faced with a broad axe. The flies, while we were building it, were something awful. Two of the men that we sent in there to build it were so badly bitten that we had to bring them out a hundred miles to a hospital. None of us saw the place while we were building it—we were all busy at the time—but the teamsters who took in our stuff said it was the worst season for the black flies that they ever remembered.

Still we hung to it, in spite of the flies, and stuck at it till we got it built. It is, as I say, only a plain place, but good enough to rough it in. We have one big room with a stone fireplace, and bedrooms round the sides, with a wide veranda, properly screened, all along the front. The veranda has a row of upright tamaracks for its posts, and doesn't look altogether bad. In the back part we have quarters where our man sleeps. We had an ice-house knocked up while they were building, and water laid on in pipes from a stream. So that, on the whole, the place has a kind of rough comfort about it—good enough, anyway, for fellows hunting moose all day.

The place, nowadays, is not hard to get at. The Government has just built a colonization highway, quite all right for motors, that happens to go within a hundred yards of our lodge.

We can get the railway for a hundred miles, and then the highway for forty, and the last hundred yards we can walk. But this season we are going to cut out the railway and go the whole way from the city in George's car, with our kit with us.

George has one of those great big cars with a roof and thick glass sides. Personally, none of the three of us would have preferred to ride in a luxurious darned thing like that. Tom says that, as far as he is concerned, he'd much sooner go into the bush over a rough trail in a buckboard; and, for my own part, a team of oxen would be more the kind of thing that I'd wish.

However, the car is there, so we might as well use the thing, especially as the provincial Government has built the fool highway right into the wilderness. By taking the big car also we can not only carry all the hunting outfit that we need, but we can also, if we like, shove in a couple of small trunks with a few clothes. This may be necessary, as it seems that somebody has gone and slapped a great big frame hotel right there in the wilderness, not half a mile from the place we go to. The hotel we find a regular nuisance. It gave us the advantage of electric light for our lodge (a thing none

of us care about), but it means more fuss about
clothes. Clothes, of course, don't really matter
when a fellow is roughing it in the bush, but Tom
says that we might find it necessary to go over to
the hotel in the evenings to borrow coal oil or a
side of bacon or any rough stuff that we need;
and they do such a lot of dressing up at these fool
hotels now, that if we do go over for bacon or
anything in the evening we might just as well slip
on our evening clothes, as we could chuck them
off the minute we get back. George thinks it
might not be a bad idea—just as a way of saving
all our energy for getting after the moose—to dine
each evening at the hotel itself. He knew some
men who did that last year, and they told him that
the time saved for moose-hunting in that way is
extraordinary. George's idea is that we could
come in each night with our moose—such-and-such
a number as the case might be—either bringing
them with us or burying them where they die,
change our things, slide over to the hotel and get
dinner, and then beat it back into the bush by
moonlight and fetch in the moose. It seems they
have a regular two-dollar table d'hôte dinner at
the hotel—just rough stuff of course, but after
all, as we all admit, we don't propose to go out
into the wilds to pamper ourselves with high feeding;
a plain hotel meal in a home-like style at two dollars

a plate is better than cooking up a lot of rich stuff over a camp-fire.

If we *do* dine at the hotel we could take our choice each evening between going back into the bush by moonlight to fetch in the dead moose from the different caches where we had hidden them, or sticking round the hotel itself for a while. It seems that there is dancing there. Nowadays such a lot of women and girls get the open-air craze for the life in the bush that these big wilderness hotels are crowded with them. There is something about living in the open that attracts modern women, and they like to get right away from everybody and everything; and, of course, hotels of this type in the open are nowadays always well closed in with screens so that there are no flies or anything of that sort.

So it seems that there is dancing at the hotel every evening, nothing on a large scale or pretentious, just an ordinary hardwood floor—they may wax it a little for all I know—and some sort of plain, rough Italian orchestra that they fetch up from the city. Not that any of us care for dancing. It's a thing that, personally, we wouldn't bother with. But it happens that there are a couple of young girls that Tom knows that are going to be staying at the hotel, and, of course, naturally he wants to give them a good time. They are only eighteen and twenty (sisters), and that's really younger than we care for, but with young girls like that—practically kids—any man wants to give them a good time. So Tom says, and I think quite rightly, that as the kids are going to be there we may as well put in an appearance at the hotel and see that they are having a good time. Their mother is going to be with them too, and of course we want to give her a good time as well; in fact, I think I will lend her my moose rifle and let her go out and shoot moose. One thing we are all agreed upon in the arrangement of our hunting trip is in not taking along anything to drink. Drinking spoils a trip of that sort. We all remember how in the old days we'd go out into a camp in the bush (I mean before there used to be any highway or any hotel), and carry in rye whisky in demi-johns (two dollars a gallon it was), and sit around the camp-fire drinking it in the evenings.

But there's nothing in it. We all agree that, the law being what it is, it is better to stick to it. It makes a fellow feel better. So we shall carry nothing in. I don't say that one might not have a flask of something in one's pocket in the car; but only as a precaution against accident or cold. And when we get to our lodge we all feel that we are a darned sight better without it. If we *should* need anything—though it isn't likely—there are still three cases of old Scotch whisky kicking around the lodge somewhere : I think they are kicking round in a little cement cellar with a locked door that we had made so as to use it for butter or anything of that sort. Anyway, there are three, possibly four, or maybe five, cases of Scotch there, and, if we should for any reason want it, there it is. But we are hardly likely to touch it—unless we hit a cold snap, or a wet spell ; then we might ; or if we strike hot, dry weather. Tom says he thinks there are a couple of cases of champagne still in the cellar—some stuff that one of us must have shot in there just before Prohibition came in. But we'll hardly use it. When a man is out moose-hunting from dawn to dusk he hasn't much use for champagne—not till he gets home, anyway. The only thing that Tom says the champagne might come in useful for would be if we cared to ask the two kids over to some sort of dinner ; it would be just a rough kind of camp dinner (we could hardly ask their mother to it), but we think we could manage it. The man we keep there used to be a butler in England, or something of the sort, and he could manage some kind of rough meal where the champagne might fit in.

There's only one trouble about our plans for our fall camp that bothers us just a little. The moose are getting damn scarce about that place.

There used, so they say, to be any quantity of them. There's an old settler up there that our man buys all our cream from, who says that he remembers when the moose were so thick that they would come up and drink whisky out of his dipper. But somehow they seem to have quit the place. Last year we sent our man out again and again looking for them, and he never saw any. Three years ago a boy that works at the hotel said he saw a moose in the cow pasture back of the hotel, and there were the tracks of a moose seen last year at the place not ten miles from the hotel where it had come to drink. But, apart from these two exceptions, the moose-hunting has been poor.

Still, what does it matter ? What we want is the *life*, the rough life, just as I have described it. If any moose comes to our lodge, we'll shoot him, or tell the butler to. But if not—well, we've got along without for ten years. I don't suppose we shall worry.

XVII—Abolishing the Heroine

(A Plea that Fewer Heroines and More Crimes would add Sprightliness to our Fiction)

I WANT to lead a bold national movement for the abolition of the Heroine from our literature. In my opinion the time has come when this young woman has grown to be a nuisance. All our stories would be much better without her. She just clutters them all up.

What I mean is this. Open any story of adventure or excitement or crime; and you find that it runs along admirably for a certain distance, but just when it is getting exciting and worth while in steps the Heroine and spoils it.

Let me give an example of what I mean. Every reader of up-to-date fiction will recognize the thing in a minute. Call the story:

AFTER MIDNIGHT

or, How the Heroine spoils a Crime Story.

Now we begin:

John Curbstone is a young bachelor club-man of great wealth. He is a man of culture, being a

graduate of Harvard University. (In all these stories Harvard is the best place to graduate them from. It sounds far better than the Minnesota Agricultural College.) He is a keen sportsman, because this enables him to wear the right kind of breeches for the illustrator to use—shaped like a ham at the hips and tight at the knee. All Harvard graduates wear them. He plays polo, golf, and bridge, would drink brandy and soda if he could get it, and has one of those clean-shaven aristocratic faces seen only in a democratic country.

He lives—with a butler who doesn't count and some servants who don't come into the story—in a large sandstone house on Riverside Drive. This family residence had belonged to Curbstone's father before him, which shows that his family is an old one. Indeed the Curbstones have lived on that street for thirty years, which gives young Curbstone a sense of *noblesse oblige* towards the whole district up to 125th Street.

The scene is now laid.

Returning home late one night from his club (he never leaves his club till it shuts), John realizes that his house has been burglarized. In the dining-room the sideboard has been rudely broken open, apparently with a jemmy. A glass, still reeking with ginger ale, rests on the top of it; an open bottle, evidently opened with a jemmy, is near it.

In the corner of the room the iron safe has been forced, most likely with a jemmy. There is a litter of bonds and family jewellery on the floor. It is clear that the burglar has been interrupted at his work. It is likely that he is still on the premises.

John Curbstone stands motionless in the centre of the room listening. There is absolute silence. There is no sound in the still house but the ticking of a clock.

Then as Curbstone listens intently, his ear just catches a faint sound from behind the closed door of a cupboard. The burglar must be there hidden behind the door! Curbstone draws his revolver from his hip (it was the revolver that he had used that night for playing poker), and levels it full at the cupboard.

" I shall count three," he announced in clear, even tones, " and if you are not out of that cupboard then, I shall fire through the door." Curbstone counted, still in clear, even tones, " One, two "— but just as he was going to say three an agitated voice exclaimed, " Oh, please don't shoot!" the cupboard door opened, and there stepped out into the room—

A girl! Just think of it, a girl! And, what makes it worse, only a mere slip of a girl! If it had been a big one—you know, one of those great

238

big, fine-looking ones, it wouldn't have been so bad. But this one is only a slip!

She came forward towards John Curbstone, her large blue eyes distracted with apprehension. She was in evening dress, with a light peignoir, or baignoire or boudoir, thrown about her shoulders. "Please don't shoot," she repeated (at this point in the story the illustrator gets in his work and doesn't have to read any further).

Curbstone lowered his revolver.

"So," he said sternly, "you are a *thief*." The girl shuddered into herself. The word seemed to sting her. She didn't mind breaking open Curbstone's safe, but when she was called a "thief" she was stung.

"I'm not a thief," she panted.

.   .   .   .   .

There! Let us leave her there a little, panting, while I talk about her. I have seen that girl come out of that cupboard and similar places so often that I'm sick of her. I know that just as soon as the man in the story opens a cupboard door, or draws aside a curtain, out comes "a slip of a girl." He hears a noise in the attic. What is there? A girl. He hears some one in the cellar. Who is it? A girl. Who did it? A girl, a mere child!

Now what I say is, that this kind of thing is ruining our best stories. They start in excitement and end in slush. In the story I have just outlined, when the cupboard door opened, Curbstone ought to have been confronted with something worth while—a burglar—a real one, with short-cropped hair under a low cap, with a dark lantern in one hand and a jemmy in the other. Then when Curbstone said sternly, " So, you are a thief," the burglar could answer, " I sure am." Or, better still, the door might open, and three burglars come out, or even four ; in short, a cupboardful of burglars. Even if it has to be a girl, why make her a " slip " ? Why not let it read : " There stepped out of the cupboard a great big girl about six feet high and at least seventeen inches around the neck." In any such case the adventure and excitement of the story could continue. There could be a tremendous fight—in which, let us hope, they might have killed Curbstone and sent him back to his club dead, and so put him out of literature for ever.

But it is understood that a man, or at least a Harvard graduate, must not use force against a slip of a girl. So, in default of a decent ending, the story has to run off into slush.

Ending it up is quite simple : it would probably be done somewhat as follows :

" I'm not a thief," she repeated.
She looked at him for a minute proudly, defiantly,

for she came of an old family just as proud as his. Her people had had the same summer cottage in the Adirondacks for six years running.

John Curbstone looked at the girl calmly. " Miss Chetwynde," he said, " if you are not a thief, will you kindly tell me why you tried to rob my safe ? " When he calls her " Miss Chetwynde," this is meant as an indication to the reader that Curbstone knows her.

" Oh, how can I explain ? " exclaimed the girl, wringing her hands. " You wouldn't understand ! you couldn't understand ! I wanted the money so much ! There is so much to do with money, so much suffering to alleviate : and you with your great wealth, you do nothing ! Ask yourself," she continued, her voice thrilled with earnestness, " what do you do for social service, for sanitation, for reafforestation, for the Girl Guides, for the Boy Scouts ? "

John Curbstone hung his head with a groan. " Nothing," he said.

" This afternoon," the girl went on, " I came to your office. I asked you for a hundred thousand dollars for the Metropolitan Police Picnic, and you refused ! "

" Miss Chetwynde," said Curbstone, in the same clear, even tones that he had used earlier, " I did *not* refuse. I asked you to marry me. It was you who did me the honour of refusal."

" It maddened me," the girl went on, " and I determined to take your money ; yes, *take* it, and give it to the Police. If that is stealing, I don't care. Then I came here to rob you. The Police themselves lent me the jemmy! Oh, it was madness, madness ! . . ."

She paused. They were both silent for a moment. Then Curbstone reached out and took her by the hand.

" Miss Chetwynde, Alice," he said, " don't you think that we have both been a little wrong ? "

She looked up timidly. " A little, John dear," she murmured.

.   .   .   .   .

And with that the story is ended, and looks just like any of the other two hundred that are published every month. But what I want is to see that disturbing girl cut out, and real adventure put in—in short, more crime and plenty of it.

XVIII—My Affair with my Landlord; or, Did I Dream it?

AS it is now pretty generally known that I have murdered the landlord of our flat, I feel that I should like to make some sort of public explanation of the matter.

I have been assured on all sides that there is no need to do this, but my own feelings on the question were so acute that I felt myself compelled to call upon the Superintendent of Police and offer him an exact account of what I had done. He told me that there is absolutely no need to offer any explanation at all. It is neither customary nor desirable.

" You have killed your landlord," he said, " very good, what of it ? "

I asked him whether it was not, in a sense, a matter for the law to deal with. But he shook his head. " In what way ? " he asked.

I told him that I felt that the affair was putting me in a somewhat false position ; that the congratulations that I have been receiving from my friends, and even from strangers, were perhaps, if the full circumstances were known, hardly merited ; in short, that I should like a certain publicity given to the whole surroundings of the act.

"Very good," said the Superintendent, "you are entitled to fill out a form if you wish to do so." He searched among his papers.

"Did you say," he asked, "that you *have* killed your landlord, or that you are *going* to kill him ? "

"I *have* killed him," I said firmly.

"Very good," said the officer, "we use separate forms."

He gave me a long printed slip with blanks to fill in—my age, occupation, reasons (if any) for the killing, etc.

"What shall I put," I asked, "under the heading of *reasons* ? "

"I think," he answered, "that it will be better to put simply, 'no reasons,' or if you like, the 'usual reasons'!" With that he bowed me politely out of his office, expressing, as he did so, the hope that I would bury the landlord and not leave him lying about.

To me the interview was unsatisfactory. I am well aware that the Superintendent was within the strict nicety of the law. No doubt if every case of the shooting of a landlord were made a matter of inquiry the result would be embarrassing and tedious.

The shooting is generally done in connection with a rise of rent, and nothing more needs to be said about it. " I am increasing your rent another four pounds a month," says the landlord. " All right," says the tenant, " I'll shoot you." Sometimes he does, sometimes he forgets to.

But my own case was quite different. The proposal of the National Tenants' League to give me a gold medal next Saturday has brought things to a head, and forces an explanation.

I recall distinctly the time, now some five years ago, when my wife and I first took our flat. The landlord showed us over it himself, and I am free to confess that there was nothing in his manner, or very little indeed, to suggest anything out of the normal.

Only one small incident stuck in my mind. He apologized for the lack of cupboard space.

" There are not enough cupboards in this flat," he said.

It made me slightly uncomfortable to hear him speak in this way. " But look," I said, " how large and airy this pantry is. It is at least four feet each way."

He shook his head and repeated that the cupboards were small. " I must build in better ones," he said.

Two months later he built in new cupboards. It gave me a shock of surprise—a touch of the uncanny—to notice that he did not raise the rent. " Are you not raising the rent because of the cupboards ? " I asked.

" No," he said, " they only cost me ten pounds."

" But, my dear fellow," I objected, " surely the interest on ten pounds is twelve pounds a year ? "

He admitted this, but said that he would rather not raise the rent. Thinking it over, I decided that his conduct might be due to incipient paresis or coagulation of the arteries of the head. At that time I had no idea of killing him. That came later.

I recall no incident of importance till the spring of the year following. My landlord appeared unexpectedly one day with apologies for intruding (a fact which of itself seemed suspicious), and said that he proposed to re-paper the entire apartment. I expostulated in vain.

" The paper," I said, " is only ten years old."

" It is," he said ; " but wall-paper has gone up to double its value since that time."

" Very good, then," I said firmly, " you must raise the rent five pounds a month for the paper."

" I shall not," he answered.

The incident led to a distinct coolness between us for some months.

The next episodes were of a more pronounced character. Everybody recalls the great increases of rent due to the terrific rise in building costs. My landlord refused to raise the rent of my flat.

" The cost of building," I said, " has increased at least 100 per cent."

" Very good," he answered, " but I am not building. I have always been getting 10 per cent on my investment in this property, and I am still getting it."

" Think of your wife," I said.

" I won't," he answered.

" It is your duty," I went on, " to think of her. Let me tell you that only yesterday I saw in the papers a letter from a landlord—one of the most beautiful letters I ever saw (from a landlord)—in which he said the rise in the cost of building materials compelled him to think of his wife and children. It was a touching appeal."

" I don't care," my landlord answered, " I am not married."

" Ah," I said, " not married." It was, I think, at this moment that the idea first occurred to me that the man might be put out of the way.

There followed the episode of November. My readers will all remember the 50 per cent increase of rents made to celebrate Armistice Day. My landlord refused to join in the celebrations.

This lack of patriotism in the fellow irritated me greatly. The same thing happened at the time of the rise of rents that was instituted to celebrate the visit of Marshal Foch, and the later rise—25 per cent, if I remember rightly—that was made as a tribute to the ex-Service men.

It was purely a patriotic movement, done in a spontaneous way without premeditation.

I have heard many of the soldiers say that it was their first welcome home, and that they would never forget it.

It was followed a little later by the rise of rents held as a welcome to the Prince of Wales. No better congratulation could have been planned.

My landlord, alas, remained outside of all this. He made no increase in his rent. " I have," he said, " my 10 per cent, and that is enough."

I know now that the paresis or coagulation must have overwhelmed one entire lobe or hemisphere of his head.

I was meditating action.

The crisis came last month. A sharp rise in rent had been very properly instituted to counterbalance the fall in the German mark. It was based quite evidently on the soundest business reasoning.

If the fall in the mark is not countered in this way, it is plain that we are undone. The cheap German mark will enable the Germans to take away our houses.

I waited for three days, looking in vain for a notice of increase in my rent.

Then I went to visit my landlord in his office. I admit that I was armed, but in extenuation I want to say that I knew that I had to deal with an abnormal, aberrated man, one-half of whose brain was now coagulated.

I wasted no words on preliminaries.

" You have seen," I said, " this fall of the German mark."

" Yes," he answered, " what of it ? "

" Simply this," I said. " Are you going to raise my rent or are you not ? "

" No," he said doggedly. " I am not."

I raised the revolver and fired. He was sitting sideways to me as I did so. I fired, in all, four shots. I could see through the smoke that one, at least, of the shots had cut his waistcoat into strips, a second had ripped off his collar, while the third and fourth had cut through his braces at the back. He was visibly in a state of collapse. It was doubtful if he could reach the street. But, even if he could, it was certain that he couldn't walk upon it.

I left him as he was, and reported, as I have said, to the police.

If the Tenants' League medal is given to me, I want it to be with full understanding of the case.

XIX—Why I refuse to play Golf

I AM old enough to remember very distinctly the first coming of the game of golf to the city where I live. It came in that insidious but forceful way that characterizes everything Scotch. It was similar to the spread of Scotch Banking, the Scotch Church, and Scotch whisky.

The exact circumstances were these. One afternoon in April, when the wind was on the new grass, three Scotchmen went out to a hill slope near the town. They carried with them three crooked sticks and a little ball. There was firmness in their manner, but nothing obviously criminal. They laid the ball down and began to beat it about on the grass. In fairness it must be admitted that they made no parade of the matter. They paid no attention to the few mystified people who watched them. At the end of about an hour they were seen to sit down under a brier bush : there they remained for some time. It was thought at the time that they were either praying or drinking whisky. Opinion was divided. But the real truth was that they had formed themselves into a Golf Club.

This, I say, was on a Saturday. Had the city been well advised these men could have been arrested on the following Monday. A judicious application of the Vagrancy Laws or rather free interpretation of the Sedition Acts might have forestalled at the outset a grave national peril.

But nothing was done. Indeed, at the moment little was thought of the matter, or, at any rate, little was manifested in the shape of public indignation or public protest. Even when six Scotchmen appeared on the ground the following Saturday, and twelve the week after, and twenty-four on the last Saturday in the month, few people, if any, realized the magnitude of what was happening. The news that a Golf Club had been formed in Montreal was presently printed, quite openly, in the newspapers as if it were an ordinary event.

One must admit, even, that a very lively curiosity mixed with something approaching to envy began to surround the afternoon gatherings of the Scotchmen. There is something in the sweep of the wind over the April grass, something in the open space and the blue sky, that conveys an insidious appeal to the lower side of a man's nature. It is difficult to sit indoors at one's desk and to know that other men are striding over the turf. Moreover, the ingenious expedient of carrying out a ball and beating it round with sticks supplied a colour of activity and purpose that acted as a drug upon the conscience. Had it not been for this use of the sticks and the ball the players would have appeared as mere loafers. But the evident earnestness with which they followed their avocation robbed it of every appearance of idleness; and the public was entirely deceived as to its character.

In short, it was not long before the game began to exercise an evident effect upon those who at first had been idle spectators. They became anxious to join in. Here and there, by a very obvious and cunning piece of policy, they were invited to try their hand. The spectator then found to his surprise the peculiar difficulty of the game. He discovered that, simple though it looked, it was not possible for him to place the ball on the ground, take a drink of Scotch whisky, and then hit it with the stick. He tried again and again, but failed each time. The natural result was that he solicited membership in the Club, and reappeared on the following Saturday with a ball and stick of his own and with a flask of whisky on his hip. The Saturday after that he turned up in a pair of knickerbocker trousers, a round tam-o'-shanter hat, and a Cluny Macpherson tartan over his shoulder; after that, as far as any general utility to the community went, the man was lost.

I remember well, some eighteen months after

the Club started, realizing how far already the movement had gone when I heard the head of our greatest bank accost the President of a railway, on St. James Street, with the words, " Hoot, mon ! it's a braw morning the day ! " Up till that time language of the sort would have come under the Criminal Code.

I have since learned that this same kind of thing was going on all over the country just as it was in my own city. Men were appearing in the business streets in the Cluny Macpherson tartan. Some even had tall feathers stuck sideways in their tam-o'-shanters. At more than one public dinner the music of the bagpipes was not only tolerated but even applauded. On every Saturday, and presently even on weekdays, men were seen lifting long bags filled with crooked sticks on to the street cars.

In those days the public at large was still innocent and ignorant. We had not even heard the word " propaganda." Otherwise we should have seen under all this a dangerous organized movement for the spread of Presbyterianism and the sale of the poetry of Robert Burns.

The original Club of which I speak soon took further steps. They erected a kind of wooden structure on the ground where they played. It was a modest affair—merely two large rooms, one a sitting-room, with easy-chairs, for talking about golf in, and the other a rest- or silence-room for thinking about golf in. The ground on which they played was supposedly public property. But any attempt at ejectment was rendered out of the question by the fact that they had enrolled among their membership all the leaders of the Bar and all the senior judges.

This last point, indeed, went strongly in their favour throughout. Even when they had left the modest building of which I speak and were spreading over the landscape, it was plain that the game of golf had insinuated itself most daringly into the structure of our legal institutions. A decision of the courts decided that the game of golf may be played on Sunday, not being a game within the view of the law, but being a form of moral effort. Another decision laid down the principle that a golf club need never close the bar, not being a bar within the legal meaning of the term, but a place of rest, insomuch as the drinks sold are not drinks as known to the statute but a form of recuperation. In the same way, the pay given to a boy attendant, or caddy, is not pay but a reward, and exempts him from the Cruelty to Children Act. The Excess Profits tax, the Licence tax, and the Property tax do not apply, it is held, to the premises of a golf club, as it is a religious institution ; and both the

Privy Council and the Supreme Courts are said to be preparing decisions to the effect that consuming whisky in or near a golf club does not constitute a breach of the law, provided that it is taken only when needed and in the proportion or quantity needed, and that it is not made the subject of treating.

But I anticipate : these decisions belong, of course, to later days. I was saying that in my own town, and no doubt everywhere else, the golf club idea, once started and established, soon spread. The original ground was abandoned. A vast stretch of beautiful land, that might easily have supported hundreds and hundreds of hogs, was laid out into a golf course. It was whispered that the ground was not purchased but seized ; this is no doubt untrue, but it is an undeniable fact that this beautiful hog pasture was presently laid out into flat lawns and greens. In reality, nothing more is needed for the driving of a golf ball except a straight piece of air two hundred yards long. But it is a nice pretence of the game that a whole landscape must be seized and occupied to the exclusion of agriculture, manufacture, and all other uses. In the case of which I speak, the vast purposelessness of the affair was concealed by the cunning device of setting out tomato cans and red flags at irregular intervals. By walking among these the players are made to appear as if pursuing some known object. The position of the flags are so contrived that each player is led in a circular course and returns at intervals to the Club-house, where he may take a drink and start again. Each set of drinks is called a " round," and of course an expert player can make a round far more rapidly than a beginner.

One large club, I say, was established. Yet even after it was definitely in operation very few people realized the way in which it was disturbing our civic life. It was noticed, indeed, that the schedule of trains of our greatest railway had undergone marked change. A great number of suburban trains were introduced, and a sharp discrimination made against transcontinental and other needless traffic. A branch line was built in a convenient situation from a natural obstacle, or bunker, for the golf course. But few people connected these changes with the fact that the President of the railway and the entire directorate were members of the golf club.

A new stage of development presently appeared. There is a certain kind of animal, so biology teaches us, which increases its numbers by simply dividing itself in two. The original animal is called, I think, an amœba. But the real type of the species is the golf club. If you put one of them out in the landscape and leave it there for a year or so, you presently come back and find two ; and if the two are left unmolested for a short period they presently turn into four. Where the landscape is especially favourable, where Nature has spread out her fertile land all ready to make bunkers and her pure streams all ready to mix with Scotch whisky, the two clubs will even turn into six.

Such has been the case in our city and, I imagine, in every other. There are now twelve golf clubs in the vicinity, with ten others being organized. The area now covered occupies, it is said, twelve thousand acres. One passes in the train from the crowded confines of the city to the wide expanses of the golf clubs. Everywhere there are little greens, and tin cans and red flags, and club members in knickerbockers. Each year the city is more and more crowded. Each year the golf area is bigger and bigger.

Nor is there any public protest. Each year more and more men, hitherto respectable, God-fearing citizens, are being caught in the lure of it. It is difficult to say just what the fascination is. But it is there. Sometimes I think that it lies in pretending to be a Scotchman. It may be that : there are so many things about the Scotch that attract—their contempt of rain, their peculiar nerve in wearing a hen's feather in their hat, their comprehensive ideas on damnation—that it may well be that the golf members are simply trying to be Scotchmen. In addition to that, I blame Harry Lauder a good deal: and undoubtedly Robert Burns has a lot to answer for. But, taking it as you will, the golf club has become a grave national menace.

In my own city we are, I suppose, beyond redemption. We have golf tournaments, golf teas, and golf dinners; golf trains and golf cars and golf motors. The use of the bagpipes is everywhere tolerated, and we eat haggis on St. Andrew's Day. But if there are any cities in which this insidious movement is still in its infancy, I can only exhort them to suppress it while there is yet time.

XX—*The Approach of the Comet:*
Do You Really Care if it Hits You?

B Y this time everybody knows that a comet is due to hit the earth early in the month of June. Last week it passed through the constellation of Capricorn, going like blue-lightning. It is now moving through Virgo, to beat—all records. At the moment of writing, it can hardly be more than a few thousand billion miles away : in short, it is right upon us. Just three weeks before the celebration of the Fourth of July the comet will hit us ; in fact, there will not be any Fourth of July. There will be nothing but a hole where it used to be.

Strangely enough, I was one of the very first people to know what was going to happen. It is my custom every now and then to visit our University Observatory, the astronomer in charge of which is a friend of mine. About three weeks ago on a clear, still night, I found him peeping and peering into his telescope with evident excitement.

"This is most gratifying," he said, rubbing his hands, "most gratifying."

" What is it ? " I asked.

" A comet," he said, " is coming straight towards us. We learned yesterday that it had been seen from the observatory at Bungwelo, in Java; there seems to be no doubt that its path is directed exactly towards us."

" Will it hit us ? " I asked.

" Undoubtedly. But astronomical interest will not centre so much in the mere moment of collision as in the antecedent period, possibly extending over thirty-six hours, during which time we shall have unparalleled opportunities of observation never enjoyed before. In fact, I may say that the thirty-six hours before the comet intersects our path will be quite unique."

" So I should think," I answered, " and no doubt the collision itself will be not half bad."

The astronomer shook his head. " The mere collision itself," he said, " or, more properly, the intersection of two orbits, will be commonplace. A colossal collision occurred in Sagittarius last year, involving probably the destruction of a star of the first magnitude. We can hardly hope for any phenomena of such prime interest in connection with our own globe. Attention will be focused chiefly upon the opportunities for testing the new theory of light during the hours just preceding the precipitation of the comet against the earth. There will undoubtedly be keen controversy in the astronomical world during that period : unfortunately it will be all too brief for adequate discussion."

" And what," I said, " will become of us after the comet has hit us ? "

" That is the most interesting question of all. But unfortunately there is no agreement on the subject. According to one school the generation of heat in the impact will resolve us into a burning nebula."

" That's nice," I said. " And what do the other schools say ? "

" According to them, we shall not be dissolved into a nebula at all, but broken into a group of, say, half a million burning asteroids composed of a nucleus of molten matter and a corona of incandescent hydrogen gas, but still revolving in our orbit with scarcely any displacement."

" Great ! " I said. " I don't wonder that you are interested. But, now, tell me : How long will it take for the comet to reach us ? "

" It is a matter of rather nice calculation," replied the astronomer. " I could hardly calculate it off-hand ; one would be compelled to use a series of logarithms."

" Use them," I said, " use them."

The astronomer began to calculate, then paused

and looked up quickly from his work. "I am assuming a constant density of the ether," he said.

"That's all right," I answered.

He worked again in silence for a while, and then again spoke.

"I am disregarding all perturbation of the outer planets," he said.

"Certainly," I said; "to Hades with them."

Presently the astronomer stopped figuring.

"Well," I asked, "what is it?"

"Speaking approximately, and assuming an elliptical path with a more or less hypothetical focus——"

"Forget it," I said. "When does the comet hit us? Stick to that."

"On the 10th of June 1923."

He spoke quite calmly; for the moment it gave me a shock.

"And who," I said, "gets it in the neck first? I mean, when the comet hits the earth, which side of the earth, which country, gets hit? Does it hit us, or does it hit the Japanese, or does it bump into Soviet Russia, or where?"

The astronomer shook his head. "I can't say," he said; "and meantime will you excuse me if I return to my telescope? There is a very interesting disturbance going on to-night among the planetary asteroids. I don't like to miss it."

263

"Yes," I answered, "and they expect the same kind of thing at the big hockey match, so I'll say good night."

I spoke cheerfully, but after I left him I felt troubled. On the street I noticed the people going to and fro, and surging in and out of the moving-picture houses, and hanging on to the tail end of the street cars—talking and chattering as if nothing was going to happen.

"Alas," I thought, "what will they do when they hear that a comet is going to strike us on the 10th of June?"

For about two weeks I carried round this terrible knowledge alone. I say "alone," because naturally the astronomical world doesn't count. They knew, of course, but they saw no particular reason for talking about it: the January disturbance among the planetary asteroids was too absorbing.

During these two weeks I bore the fate of the world all alone. It seemed dreadful to think that on the 10th of June it would all be over, and that the world that I had known would end in a collision, and that some of my friends would be dissolved into a nebula and others turned into molten asteroids enveloped in a corona of incandescent hydrogen. The situation had, I admit, a few advantages. I raised a note at my bank payable on the 11th of June with a peculiar sense of gratification; and at my club at meal-times it was pleasant to look round the room at certain members (I must not name them) and reflect that they would soon be enveloped in a corona of hydrogen.

But take it all in all, it was a depressing period.

And then, strangely enough, the entire outlook altered. The astronomers having finished their calculations—about a month ago, as everybody remembers—announced to the public that the comet was coming straight at us and was due to hit us; and to my surprise, I heard a man only last night telling another about it as they hung on the straps of a street car. " I see," he said, " that a comet is due to hit us in the month of June. You didn't notice it ? It was in the paper this afternoon. It seems it is coming straight at us, and it is to collide with us on the 10th, I think it said; anyway, some time early in June." And at this they both laughed.

I find the same attitude everywhere. I heard a little boy last Sunday, on his way into church, say to his mother, " Mother, is it true that a comet is going to hit the world ? " And she said, " Yes, dear, the newspapers say so." " And where shall we be after it hits us ? " " I suppose, darling," she answered, with a touch of reverence, I admit, in her voice, " that we shall be dissolved into a nebular nucleus with an enveloping corona of incandescent hydrogen." After that they passed into church, and I heard no more.

The situation puzzles me. Here we are about to crash into a comet in a few months' time, and nobody seems to worry at all. The world goes on its way as if nothing were going to happen. In my own town we are going on building a new hotel to accommodate a thousand guests. Why ? Where will those guests be after the comet hits them ? Asteroids. In Washington they are starting preparations now for the Fourth of July. What will be left of the Fourth of July when it comes ? Gas, and nothing else.

If I were a psychologist I should start up theories about the impossibility of frightening all the people all the time : I would explain that as long as everybody is going to be destroyed all together nobody minds it : it's only the invidiousness of being destroyed alone that is distressing. In fact, I find that now that the others don't mind I don't care either. I have raised a second note at the bank payable on the 11th of June, and as a matter of fact, if the world is not destroyed on the 10th, I shall be, personally, a rather worse kind of asteroid than if it is.

Perhaps right there is the explanation of what is happening. We have got this unhappy world into such a miserable condition that in our hearts we don't care if it is destroyed or not. We've got war debts to pay that run up to 300,000,000,000 dollars : we've got the Housing Question, and the Irish Question, and the Navy Question, and Bolshevism and Socialism and Atavism : the Treaty of Sèvres is broken, the German mark is falling, the League of Nations is creaking—in short, if the comet *does* hit us, who cares ?

.   .   .   .   .

When I had written all that, I took the manuscript over to a friend at the observatory to see if I had got the astronomical part of it right. And he says that it is wrong. He says that I have misunderstood things. It seems that we don't *hit* the comet, in the sense that ordinary plain people understood it, at all. He says that the intersection of our orbits will be confined to a conjunction of our path with the corona of the comet's tail, or words to that effect. I asked him if we shall know it when it happens, and he said that by going up to the top of a high building and looking through a piece of smoked glass towards the constellation of Virgo the comet will be visible, presenting the appearance of a speck of dust with its tail comparable to the wing of a mosquito.

That's pretty small business for a world catastrophe, isn't it ? As for me, having got used to the idea of destruction, I am worried now about the 11th of June.

XXI—Personal Experiments with the Black Bass

IT was my good fortune to spend a large part of the summer just past in fishing for bass. The season may be regarded as now definitely closed, and the time is appropriate for a scientific summarizing of the results achieved and the information gained.

In my own case I venture to think that the experiments which I carried on are of especial interest to the readers of this book, insomuch as a large part of them were conducted in the immediate presence of so well-known a man as Mr. John Counsell, of Hamilton, Ontario, who acted as my assistant. Mr. Counsell very kindly permits me to say that all statements, measurements, and estimates of weight contained in the following discussion are personally vouched for by him. He has even offered to lend his oath, or any number of his oaths, to the accuracy of my statements. But it has been thought wiser not to use Mr. Counsell's oath in print.

268

I take this opportunity in turn to express my high appreciation of the hardihood, the endurance, and the quiet courage manifested by my assistant throughout our experiments. If Mr. Counsell was ever afraid of a bass I never knew it. I have seen him immersed in mud on the banks of the river where we fished; I have observed him submerged under rapids; I have seen Mr. Counsell fall from the top of rocks into water so deep and remain under so long, that I was just cranking up our car to go home, and yet I never knew him to hesitate for a moment to attack a black bass at sight and kill it.

I can guarantee to anybody who is hesitating whether or not to invite Mr. Counsell to go fishing that he is a man who may safely be taken anywhere where the bass are, and is an adornment to any party of sportsmen.

I turn therefore with added confidence to the tabulated results drawn by myself and Mr. Counsell from our experiments.

In the first place, we are able to throw much light on the vexed question as to the circumstances under which the bass bite. There has been a persistent belief that during the glare of the middle part of the day the bass do not bite. This belief is correct. They do not. It is also true that in the sunnier part of the morning itself the black bass do not, or does not, bite. Nor do they, or rather does it, bite during the more drowsy part of the afternoon.

Let the angler, therefore, on a day when the sun is bright in a cloudless sky, lay aside his rod from eight in the morning till six in the afternoon. On such a day as this the fish do not bite. The experienced angler knows this. He selects a suitable tree, lies down beneath it, and waits. Nor do the bass, oddly enough, bite, on a cloudy day. The bass dislike clouds. Very often the appearance of a single cloud on the horizon is a sign for the experienced angler to retire to a quiet spot upon the bank and wait till the cloud goes by. It has been said that the bass bite well in the rain. This is an error. They don't.

Another popular error that ought, in the interest of the young angler, to be dispelled is that the bass bite in the evening ; that is not so. The bass loves the day, and at the first sign of darkness it sinks to the bottom of the water from which it obstinately refuses to move.

I am well aware that the young angler might find himself seriously discouraged at what has just been said. "What, then," he might ask, "do the bass never bite at all ? Is it never possible to get a bite from them ? " To this I answer very positively that they both do and it is.

The results, in fine, of the experiments carried

on by Mr. Counsell and myself lead us to the conclusion that the bass bites at midnight. We offer this only as a preliminary hypothesis, for which perhaps a more ample verification will be found in the season of 1924. We ourselves have never fished till midnight. And we have observed that even the most persistent angler, as the darkness gathers around him, becomes discouraged, and at some time before midnight quits. Here he is in error. Our advice to the angler in all such cases is to keep on until midnight. The black bass, which is chary of biting in the glare of the day and which dislikes the cool of the evening, must, we argue, be just in the mood needed at midnight.

Nor let the young angler run away with the idea that the black bass never bites in the daytime. If he (young angler) does this, he must be hauled in again on the reel of actual experience. They do and they have. I recall in particular one case in point in the experiments of Mr. Counsell and myself. At the time of which I speak we were fishing from a rocky ledge at the edge of the river that is the scene of our operations. The circumstances were most propitious. The hour was just before daylight, so that there was still an agreeable sense of chilliness in the air. It was raining heavily as we took our places on the rock. Much of this rain, though not all of it, had gone down our shirts.

There had been a certain amount of lightning, two cracks of which had hit Mr. Counsell in the neck. In short, the surroundings were all that the most ardent fisherman could desire.

For the moment the rain cleared, a first beam of sunlight appeared through the woods on the bank, and at that very moment Mr. Counsell called to me that he had a bite. I immediately dropped my rod into the river, and urged Mr. Counsell to avoid all excitement ; to keep as calm as possible, and to maintain his hold upon his line. Mr. Counsell in turn exhorted me to be cool, and assured me of his absolute readiness should the fish bite again to take whatever action the circumstances might seem to us to warrant. I asked him in the meantime whether he was prepared to give me an idea of the dimensions of the fish which had bitten him. He assured me that he could, and to my great delight informed me that the fish was at least three feet long. The reader may imagine, then, with what suppressed excitement Mr. Counsell and I waited for this monster to return and bite again. Nor had we long to wait. Not more than two or three minutes had elapsed when I suddenly saw my assistant's line in violent commotion, Mr. Counsell exerting his whole strength in a magnificent combat with the fish. I called to Mr. Counsell to be cautious, and adjured him to the utmost calmness, running up and down on the bank and waving my arms to emphasize what I said. But there was no need for such an exhortation. Mr. Counsell had settled down to one of those steady fights with the black bass which are the proudest moments in the angler's life. The line was now drawn absolutely taut and motionless. Mr. Counsell was exerting his full strength at one end, and the fish, apparently lying at a point of vantage at the very bottom of the river, was exerting its full strength at the other.

But here intervened one of those disappointments which the angler must learn to bear as best he may. The bass is nothing if not cunning. And an older, larger fish of the extraordinary size and mass of the one in question shows often an almost incredible strategy in escaping from the hook. After a few minutes of hard strain my assistant suddenly became aware that the fish had left his hook, and at the very moment of escaping had contrived to fasten the hook deep into a log at the bottom of the river. Investigation with a pike pole showed this to be the case. This trick on the part of the bass is, of course, familiar to all experienced anglers. It was fortunate in this case that Mr. Counsell had contrived to get such an accurate estimate of the size of the fish before it escaped.

The young angler may well ask how it is that we are able to know the size of a fish as soon as it bites, without even the slightest glimpse of it. To this I can merely answer that we do know. It is, I suppose, an instinct. The young angler will get it himself if he goes on fishing long enough.

Nor need it be supposed that there is anything unusual or out of the way in the means of escape adopted by the particular bass in question. Indeed, I have on various occasions known the bass not merely to contrive to pass the hook into a log, but even, after it has been firmly hooked, to substitute a smaller fish than itself. I recall in particular one occasion when Mr. Counsell called to me that he had a fish. I ran to his side at once, encouraging and exhorting him as I did so. In this instance the fish came towards the top of the water with a rush : we were both able to distinguish it clearly as it moved below the surface. It was a magnificent black bass, measuring seventeen inches from its face to its tail, and weighing two and a half pounds. The gleam of its scales as it shot through the foaming water is a sight that I shall not readily forget. The fish dived low. Meantime, Mr. Counsell had braced himself so as to exert his full strength, and I placed myself behind him with my arms around his body to prevent the fish from dragging him into the stream. By this strategy the fish was thrown clear up on the rock, where Mr. Counsell attacked it at once and beat the breath out of it with a boat-hook. But judge of our surprise when we found that the fish landed was not the fish originally caught on the hook. The bass had contrived in its downward plunge to free itself from the hook and to replace itself by a yellow perch six inches long.

From what has been said above, it is only too clear that the life of the black bass fisherman has its disappointments and its hardships. The black bass is wary and elusive, more crafty, for example, than the lobster, and a gamer fighter than the sardine. The angler must face danger and discomfort. He gets rained upon : he falls into the river : he gets struck by lightning. But, for myself, when the ice of the winter has cleared away and the new season opens up, I ask no better fate than to be out again at daybreak with Mr. Counsell sitting on a rock beside the river, with the rain soaking into our shirts, waiting for a bite.

XXII—L'Envoi: To a Faded Actor
(*A Dedication*)

I CAN call him to my mind as I have seen him burlesqued and parodied a hundred times—the Faded Actor. There he stands in his bell-shaped coat, drawn in at the waist and ample in the skirt. The battered hat that he handles in his elaborate gestures, and holds against his heart as he bows, is but the wreck of a hat that was. His faded trousers are tight upon his leg, drawn downwards with a strap, and carrying some lingering suggestion of the days of Beau Brummell and George IV. His ample buttons are pieced out with string. His frilled cuffs are ostentatious in their raggedness.

From top to toe his creators have made a guy of him, a mean parody of forgotten graces. When he speaks, his voice is raucous and rotund. There is something of Shakespeare in it, and something of gin. His face is a blossom that has bloomed over-much. His feet move in long shoes, fitless, and so worn that he slides noiseless across the stage.

Beneath his arm, as if to complete the pathos of his figure, is the rolled-up manuscript of the play that he has composed and that the managers, shame be to them, refuse to produce.

In a thousand plays and parodies you shall see this figure of the Faded Actor, a stock object of undying ridicule. It is a signal for our laughter when he takes a drink, fawning to get it and swallowing it as if into a funnel ; it is a signal for our laughter when he cadges for a coin, the smallest not coming amiss ; when he arranges with elaborate care upon his uplifted wrist the ruins of his cuff ; and most of all when he draws forth from beneath his arm his manuscript and stands forth to read what none will hear except in mockery, with his poor self carried away unconscious with the art of it.

Mark him now as he strikes his attitude to read. Hear the full voice, deep and resonant for all the gin that is in it. No parody can quite remove the majesty of that, nor the grace that has once lived in those queer gestures. Let us temper our laughter, as we look upon him, with something kindlier than mockery, something nearer to respect ; for in the Faded Actor, with his strange twists and graces, his futile manuscript, his blighted hopes, his unredeemed ambitions, we are looking upon all that is best in the great traditions of the stage. That thick, deep voice—comic now, but once revered : that is the surviving tradition of the Elizabethan tragedy, declaimed as a Shakespeare or a Marlowe would have had it. That sliding step, so funny to our eye, is all that lingers of the dainty grace of the eighteenth century, when dance and stage were one ; or that dragging limp with which the poor Faded Actor crosses the stage— he does not know it, but that has come to him from Garrick ; or see that long gesticulation of the hand revealing the bare wrist below the cuff, there was a time when such gesticulation was the admired model of a Fox or a Sheridan, and held, even at second hand, the admiration of a senate.

Nay more, there is a thing in the soul of the Faded Actor that all may envy who in this life are busied with the æsthetic arts. For, after all, what does he want, poor battered guy, with his queer gestures and his outlandish graces ? Money ? Not he. He has never had, nor ever dreamed of it. A coin here and there, enough to buy a dram of gin or some broad, cheap writing-paper on which to inscribe his thoughts—that much he asks ; but beyond that his ambition never goes, for it travels elsewhere and by another road. His soul at least is pure of the taint that is smeared across the arts by the money rewards of a commercial age. He lived too soon to hear of the millions a year that crown success and kill out genius, that substitute publicity for fame, that tempt a man to do the work that pays and neglect the promptings of his soul, and that turn the field of the arts into one great glare of notoriety and noise. Not so worked and lived a Shakespeare or a Michael Angelo ; and the Faded Actor descends directly from them. Art for Art's sake is his whole creed, unconscious though it be. Some one to listen to his lines, an audience though only in a barn or beside the hedgerow, a certain meed of praise that is the breath of art and the inspiration of effort ; this he asks and no more. A yacht, a limousine, a place beside the sea—of these things the Faded Actor has never heard. A shelter in some one else's premises, enough gin to keep his voice as mellow as Shakespeare would have wished it, and, with that, permission to recite his lines, and to stand forth in his poor easy fancy as a King of Carthage, or a Sultan of Morocco. Such is the end and aim of his ambition. But out of such forms of ambition has been built up all that is best in art.

To him, then, I dedicate this book. He will never read it. But that matters nothing. I dedicate it all the same.

SOME PRESS OPINIONS OF
STEPHEN LEACOCK

"Beneficent contributions to the gaiety of nations. A blend of delicious fooling and excellent satire. . . . Those of us who are grateful to Stephen Leacock as an intrepid purveyor of wholesome food for laughter have not failed to recognise that he mingles shrewdness with levity—that he is, in short, wise as well as merry."—*Spectator*.

"There is a laugh on every page."—*Daily Sketch*.

"Like all real humorists, Stephen Leacock steps at once into his proper position. His touch of humour will make the Anglo-Saxon world his reader. . . . He certainly bids fair to rival the immortal Lewis Carroll."—*Pall Mall Gazette*.

"Here is wit, fun, frolic, nonsense, verse, satire, comedy, criticism—a perfect gold-mine for those who love laughter. Stephen Leacock's fun is fine and delicate, full of quaint surprises guaranteed to provoke cheerfulness in the dullest. He is a master-humorist."—*Daily Chronicle*.

"There is so much keen criticism running through the fun of it that Stephen Leacock strikes me as one of the last genuine philosophers, as well as one of the last great humorists."—*Evening Standard*.

"Delightful spontaneity. There is genuine gold here on every page."—*Punch*.

"In my opinion Stephen Leacock is one of the greatest humorists of our time. He is not only a great humorist, he is a great satirist, good natured, polished, artistic. In fact Mr. Leacock is a public benefactor."—*Clarion*.

JOHN LANE THE BODLEY HEAD LTD., VIGO ST., W. 1